MOLECULES IN MOTION

by

T. G. COWLING

M.A., D.Phil., F.R.S.

PROFESSOR OF APPLIED
MATHEMATICS, THE
UNIVERSITY, LEEDS

1950

HUTCHINSON'S UNIVERSITY LIBRARY

Hutchinson House, London, W.1

New York   *Melbourne*   *Sydney*   *Cape Town*

THIS VOLUME IS NUMBER 44 IN
HUTCHINSON'S UNIVERSITY LIBRARY

*Printed in Great Britain
by The Anchor Press, Ltd.,
Tiptree, Essex*

CONTENTS

INTRODUCTION

THE object of this book is to give an account of such properties of a gas as can be explained by supposing the gas to consist of molecules in motion. The first three chapters are mainly historical, explaining why scientists came to believe that a gas consists of molecules in motion. Next follow chapters discussing a variety of properties of a gas; finally, a series of applications of the general theory are set out.

The book has been written by a mathematician, and as such it naturally stresses mathematical methods. But it is not a mathematical book in the sense of teaching mathematical technique; here such technique is employed in order to understand how nature works. Nature cannot be understood simply from mathematical calculations; as is emphasized in the historical chapters, pure reason, unassisted by experiment, has often led scientists astray; but the true meaning of experimental results can often only become fully manifest when a mathematical argument is available with which to compare them. The proper line of approach is neither that of the mathematician working without contact with experiment, nor that of the experimenter carrying out measurements to a steadily increasing degree of accuracy without enlightenment as to their meaning, but a middle course in which theorist and experimenter co-operate in building up a fruitful conception of the way in which nature works. It is this middle course which I have tried to depict, even though from a mathematician's standpoint.

To read this book easily, some acquaintance with the elements of physics and chemistry is required, and a knowledge of the basic ideas of mechanics, such as force, momentum, and energy, is almost essential. I have tried to make as few demands as possible on the mathematical attainments of the reader. Where advanced ideas are employed they are explained as introduced; where such an explanation is impossible the mathematical argument is not given in detail, but only its general course is outlined. The ideas on which a mathematical proof depends can often be explained simply when their detailed working out would lead to extreme complications; and in such cases I have simply recounted the basic arguments.

CHAPTER I

THE EARLY DAYS OF THE
ATOMIC THEORY

The Beginnings

THE first to speak of atoms were ancient Greeks; the word "atom" comes from a Greek word meaning "indivisible". An atomic theory was part of the belief of the Epicurean philosophers: we know of it chiefly through the works of the Roman poet Lucretius.

The Greeks thought of atoms because they believed that matter must be indestructible. Rocks and other solid bodies break to pieces or wear away; but, as Lucretius put it, something must remain immutable lest all things be utterly reduced to nothingness. So the atomists taught that, though large bodies are not immutable, they consist of tiny hard particles which themselves are eternal and unchangeable. The hard particles they called atoms; of atoms, they said, were composed not only the material bodies, but also the soul, fire, etc.

Atoms were supposed to be of many kinds, different in shape, size and weight. Atoms of fire were the smallest and roundest; atoms of the soul, renewed as we breathe, were similar; atoms of man's bodily envelope were coarse. Atoms could remain free, or hook on to others to form more or less permanent bodies. In either case they were in rapid motion, moving with the speed of thought. Free atoms moved nearly in straight lines, every now and then colliding with other atoms and bouncing off. Atoms in bodies wriggled to and fro, so far as the hooks holding them to other atoms would allow. In addition to the atoms, space was also supposed to be filled with particle-like "images", emitted by one body and received by others, whereby the properties of the first, such as its colour, size, and warmth, could become known to the beholder.

The apparently continuous properties of ordinary matter were reconciled with its atomic make-up by supposing the atoms to be extremely tiny. Lucretius compared matter in bulk to a large flock of sheep on a hillside, which from a distance appears as a stationary, continuous white patch, even though the individual sheep are moving about and the lambs skipping. The individual atoms, he said, were far too small to be seen separately; a gold ring wears away in years without ever suffering a visible loss of matter; a rock is worn down imperceptibly by the tramp of many feet; clothes become wet with dew without any visible water drops falling on them, and similarly dry in the sun; and so on.

Greek belief in the atomic theory rested on very few solid facts. It was not really a scientific theory in the modern sense. It was scientific only in its presupposition that all events are the outcome of natural law; it was unscientific in that it did not rest on experiment, and its least verifiable parts, like the statement that the soul consisted of small, round atoms, were asserted as dogmatically as those parts which seemed more probable. Like other theories of Greek philosophy, it was constructed by arguing logically from certain basic dogmas; these dogmas, though suggested by well-known facts, were not the only beliefs consistent with those facts. For example, it was just as reasonable—perhaps more reasonable in the existing state of knowledge—to suppose with Aristotle that matter does not consist of atoms, but is continuous, filling all space.

Aristotle and His School

Aristotle, like many other Greeks before him, taught that all matter was composed of four elements—earth, water, air and fire—mixed in different proportions. The different elements had different attributes—earth being cold and dry, water cold and wet, air hot and wet, and fire hot and dry. By altering its attributes one element could be transmuted into another. Each element sought its own kind and its own place, the natural place of one element being above that of another: for example, after dirty water is stirred the earth sinks to the bottom, and bubbles of air rise to the top.

Aristotle was a great scientist in the modern sense of the term; he did not try simply to invent theories, but to collect facts and test whether theories agreed with those facts. But he was a biologist rather than a physicist, and he tended sometimes to endow dead matter with the attributes of living beings. He thought of material attractions and repulsions as akin to love and hate; and material bodies behaved as they did, in his way of thinking, almost because they were conscious of a purpose within them. He insisted that living beings must be treated as organic wholes, and could not simply be considered as aggregates of separate little bits. Thus, when he turned to physics, he likewise rejected the subdivision of matter into atoms.

His interpretation of nature was full of a belief in purpose; ultimately, for him, nature moved as it did because of the plan and purpose of its creator. His outlook was religious, though with his strong sense of the orderliness of nature he opposed many of the current religious beliefs of the day. The gods of the common people in his day were beings always ready to interfere in everyday life in unpredictable, and often unpleasant, ways. This, indeed, was why the Epicureans tried to explain nature in terms of moving atoms; they felt that reasonable codes of moral conduct were impossible in a universe subject to arbitrary interference at every turn. Their outlook was essentially godless. They did not actually deny that there might be gods—composed of atoms, like the rest of the universe—but they did deny that the actions of these gods affected the lives of ordinary men and women.

During the dark ages which followed the break-up of the Roman Empire the writings of all the ancient Greeks were forgotten in western Europe. When they were rediscovered in the Middle Ages Aristotle's philosophy, with its underlying religious outlook, was quickly incorporated into Christian doctrine, and received the stamp of orthodoxy. By the sixteenth century, to doubt Aristotle had become a dangerous heresy, nearly as grave as to question the Church's authority. And, of course, the parts of his teaching which received most veneration were not his spirit of unfettered enquiry and his tireless study of nature, but his assertions about matters of which he had no direct knowledge, like the motions of the heavenly bodies. Instead of an inspiring teacher, he had become a dictator. The good Aristotelian, wondering how many teeth a horse had, would not think of examining the horses in his own stable; he would consult the Master first.

By contrast the atomic theory, with its godless associations, was on the list of heresies. The first modern atomist was Giordano Bruno, in the sixteenth century. It was not his only heresy; he was a Dominican monk who abandoned his monastic calling, and, in a time when Europe was rent between Catholic and Protestant, he had no use for either; he also bitterly attacked Aristotle's philosophy. He ended as a victim of the Inquisition (A.D. 1600). Before the merits of the atomic theory could be fairly assessed the unquestioning acceptance of Aristotle's views had to end, and the atomic theory had to be freed from its association with godlessness.

Modern Beginnings

The attack on Aristotle came from many sides. He had made a number of minor assertions which could be shown to be wrong. Such a fact, while hardly detracting from the scientific value of his work, made its dogmatic acceptance ultimately impossible.

Aristotle said that bodies fell because each tried to find its own level; the heavier the body the faster must it fall. Galileo, by dropping a large weight and a small one from the Leaning Tower of Pisa, showed that bodies of different weights fell at exactly the same rate. Galileo also used his new telescope to show that the planet Jupiter had moons; good Aristotelians did not want to accept their existence, since the Master had not mentioned them. Finally Galileo, following Copernicus, showed that a much simpler picture of the universe was got by supposing the earth to move round the sun, and rotate round its axis, than by supposing it to be at rest at the centre of the universe, as Aristotle taught. This was too much for the Aristotelians; Galileo was summoned before the Inquisition and forced to recant.

Others took up the cudgels. Dogmas of all kinds were becoming less respected by the middle of the seventeenth century, particularly after the religious wars had led to a measure of religious freedom in some countries, and heartily sickened many of intolerance. P. Gassendi (1592–1655) succeeded in advocating the atomic theory while still remaining an orthodox Catholic. He put forward little which was not derived from ancient authors; he still held that heat consists of special atoms, and that sound is transmitted by other special atoms. But he was able, in large measure, to free the atomic theory from the odour of irreligion which still clung round it; as a French writer has put it, he made the atoms Christians. His direct contribution to the struggle against Aristotle was to show that all sounds travel at the same speed, whereas Aristotle asserted that high notes must travel faster than low.

Boyle came next, with experiments on the pressure and weight of the air (1660). Aristotle taught that air tends to rise above earth and water simply because it seeks its own level. Boyle showed that air has weight, like earth and water, and its tendency to sink is in no wise different from theirs. Again, the Aristotelians taught that mercury in a barometer tube and water in a pump are sucked up because nature abhors a vacuum; Boyle showed that they are pushed up by the weight of the air pushing on the free surface.

Newton entered the controversy when he showed that white light could be divided into all the colours of the rainbow. Aristotle had taught that all colours were mixtures of light and dark in different proportions, and Newton was so vigorously assailed by indignant Aristotelians that he was reluctant ever after to publish his scientific work lest it should bring another hornets' nest about him. As he said, his business was not to invent hypotheses, but to ascertain the laws according to which nature worked; the Aristotelians did not seem to recognize the distinction between hypothesis and ascertained fact. But, even if they did not, others did, and so dogmatic belief in Aristotle's system died quietly during the second half of the seventeenth century.

There were many candidates to succeed it. Undeterred by Aristotle's failure, many, like Gassendi, Descartes, and Leibniz, sought to develop a system explaining the behaviour of the whole universe, building it each time on a few elementary and reasonable suppositions. The danger of this method, as Boyle pointed out, was that at best men would not be "solicitous to gather experiments to prove their doctrines, but rather to illustrate them", and at worst they would deny the correctness of observed facts sooner than abandon their cherished beliefs. Boyle himself, like Hooke and Newton among his contemporaries, thought an atomic theory to be very reasonable; but he realized that experiments were necessary before it could be more than a hypothesis among other hypotheses, many of them also attractive and plausible.

This emphasis on experiment was the new characteristic of the age. Though it was still fashionable to invent systems for the universe, scientists were recognizing more and more that their chief duty was less ambitious; it was, rather, to discover and co-ordinate new facts, so as to be able to predict with certainty how small parts of nature would behave in known circumstances. This represented a great and, to many, undesirable, restriction of the aims of science. But it did make possible, for the first time, an ultimate decision between a true hypothesis and a false. No such decision is possible until it is known which cause produces a particular effect, and what is the exact effect of a special cause.

A decision on the correctness of the atomic theory was not to come for another century, since chemistry was not yet sufficiently far developed for decisive experiments. But even now the theory could be used, and was used, to explain certain experimental facts—those relating to the pressure of a gas.

Boyle's Law

The pressure of a gas is the force per unit area which it exerts on any body, or across any surface drawn within it. The pressure is the same in all directions at any special point, and can usually be taken as the same at all points of a small volume of gas.

The fundamental experimental law regarding the pressure of a gas is Boyle's celebrated law (1662), that for a given mass of gas at a given temperature the pressure is inversely proportional to the volume. Boyle described his law as "the hypothesis which supposes pressures and expansions to be in reciprocal proportion". On the continent the law is often known after Mariotte, who stated it in 1676 in the form "*L'air se condense à proportion des poids dont il est chargé.*" It is questionable, however, if Mariotte can be credited with the independent discovery of the law.

Boyle's own explanation of the pressure of the air, given in 1660, was as follows: "This notion may perhaps be somewhat further explained by conceiving the air . . . to be such a heap of little bodies, lying one upon another, as may be resembled to a fleece of wool. For this . . . consists of many slender and flexible hairs, each of which may indeed, like a little spring, be still endeavouring to stretch itself out again. For though both these hairs and the aerial corpuscles to which we liken them do easily yield to external pressures, yet each of them (by virtue of its structure) is endowed with a power or principle of self-dilatation." That is, Boyle supposed the air to consist of atoms touching each other, and its pressure to be due to the springiness of the atoms. But this suggestion, though able in general terms to explain why gas could exert a pressure, could not explain Boyle's law without further assumptions.

Newton, in his *Principia* (1687), suggested that gas pressures might be due to forces between atoms not in contact, and showed that, in special circumstances, Boyle's law could be explained by supposing atoms to repel each other with a force inversely proportional to the distance between them. He was very careful not to assert that molecules did, in fact, repel each other like this, saying that this was a question which physicists must decide; but some of his followers were less cautious. In fact, a repulsive force varying inversely as the distance would imply that the chief part of the force on a special atom would be contributed by atoms at relatively great distances, and that, contrary to experiment, the pressure would depend on the shape of the vessel containing the gas.

Of all Boyle's contemporaries, Hooke (1678) came closest to the modern explanation of Boyle's law. He regarded a gas as composed of atoms each moving to and fro in its own "Vibrative Space", the limits of its to-and-fro motions being determined by "Occursions", i.e. collisions with other atoms. He supposed the pressure exerted by the gas on the vessel containing it to be due to the repeated pushes exerted by the atoms when they collide with the vessel's walls; there was a similar pressure across any surface inside the gas, due to the pushes exerted during collisions by atoms on one side of the surface on atoms on the other. If the volume of the vessel were decreased, each atom would have a shorter distance to travel between two successive pushes, the pushes would become more frequent, and the pressure would increase. As Hooke put it, if a quantity of a gas "be enclosed by a solid body, and that be so contrived as to compress it into less room, the motion thereof . . . will continue the same, and consequently the vibrations and occursions will be increased in reciprocal proportion. . . . Again, if the containing vessel be so contrived as to leave it more space . . . the number of vibrations and occursions will be reciprocally diminished."

The time was not yet ripe for ideas like these, and they were soon forgotten. They were suggested independently, and with modifications, by D. Bernoulli (1738), and were again ignored. They received general acceptance only about the year 1850, when they were again advanced by a number of scientists, of whom Joule and Clausius were the most prominent. Clausius's discussion was substantially the modern one.

In these days the small particles composing a gas are called molecules, not atoms. The modern explanation of the pressure of a gas on the containing vessel, like Hooke's, is that it originates from the pushes exerted on the vessel by molecules colliding with it. The pushes are too small, and take place in too rapid a succession, for them to be distinguished separately; the observed pressure is the smoothed effect of the pushes. The modern explanation of the pressure across a surface inside the gas, however, differs somewhat from Hooke's, since his "vibrative spaces" have no counterpart in modern ideas about gases. The molecules are very small, and are separated by relatively great open spaces; their actual volume takes up only a small part of the volume containing the gas, most of the latter volume being empty. A molecule is not confined to any special region, but moves along an intricate path among the others; it shoots past several other molecules before finding one with which to collide, and then bounces off in a direction more or less unrelated to its original direction.

We shall now break into our historical account to explain how the pressure of a gas can be calculated mathematically on the basis of the atomic theory. First of all, however, it is necessary to introduce certain basic mathematical ideas.

Co-ordinates and Vectors

Because a gas molecule is so tiny, its size can often be completely neglected, and it can be said to be at a particular point. Its position is usually fixed by using three co-ordinate axes. These are three lines Ox, Oy, Oz mutually at right angles, through a point O called the origin; for example, Oz could be vertical, and Ox, Oy two perpendicular horizontal lines. The point P occupied by a molecule is fixed by its distances

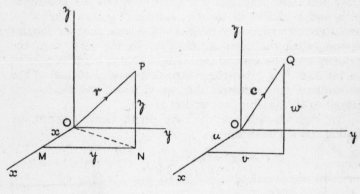

Fig. 1a   Fig. 1b

Components of the displacement and velocity vectors.

x, y, z from the co-ordinate planes yOz, zOx, and xOy (see Fig. 1a); these distances are called its three co-ordinates. If x is known, P must lie on a plane parallel to yOz, and distant x from it. When x, y, and z are all known, P is fixed as the intersection of this plane and two similar planes parallel to zOx and xOy.

A quantity possessing both size and direction is called a vector. For example, the displacement OP of P from O, considered as possessing direction as well as length, is a vector called the displacement-vector of P. The velocity of a molecule is a second vector. Any vector can be represented by a line OQ drawn from the origin O, the direction of OQ being that of the vector, and the length OQ being proportional to the vector's size. A vector is denoted by a symbol in heavy type, its size being specified by the same symbol in italics; for example, the displacement-vector of P is denoted by $\mathbf{r}$, while the length OP is denoted by r. Again, the velocity of a molecule is denoted by $\mathbf{c}$; when, however, we are not concerned with the direction in which the molecule is moving, but only with the rate at which it is travelling, we speak of the *speed c*.

The displacement $\mathbf{r}$ from O to P can be made up from three successive displacements OM, MN, and NP of lengths x, y, and z parallel to Ox, Oy, and Oz (Fig. 1a). Thus x, y, and z give the parts of $\mathbf{r}$ parallel to the axes; they are for this reason called the components of $\mathbf{r}$. In the same way, the velocity $\mathbf{c}$ can be divided into components u, v and w parallel to the axes (Fig. 1b); the component parallel to one of the co-ordinate axes measures the rate at which the molecule is travelling in the direction of that axis.

In Fig. 1a, ON and NP are perpendicular; hence, by Pythagoras's Theorem,

$$r^2 = OP^2 = ON^2 + NP^2$$
$$= OM^2 + MN^2 + NP^2$$
$$= x^2 + y^2 + z^2, \qquad . \qquad . \qquad . \qquad (1)$$

and similarly

$$c^2 = u^2 + v^2 + w^2. \qquad . \qquad . \qquad . \qquad (2)$$

The kinetic energy of a molecule due to the velocity $\mathbf{c}$ is defined as $\frac{1}{2} mc^2$, where m is its mass; thus it is

$$\tfrac{1}{2} m (u^2 + v^2 + w^2),$$

that is, it equals the sum of the kinetic energies $\frac{1}{2} mu^2$, $\frac{1}{2} mv^2$, and $\frac{1}{2} mw^2$ of the component velocities u, v, and w taken separately.

Surface and Internal Pressures

Consider now the pressure which a gas exerts on the vessel which encloses it. The actual volume of the molecules is supposed to be negligible compared with the total volume of the vessel, nearly all of this volume being full of emptiness.

Also the state of the gas is supposed to be uniform, steady and isotropic; that is, there is nothing to distinguish one point of the gas, one time, or one direction of motion of the molecules from any other.

The track of a molecule consists of a series of straight paths terminated by collisions with other molecules. The gas

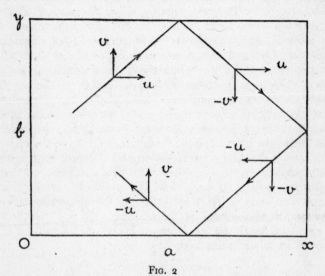

Fig. 2

Path of a molecule in a rectangular box with reflecting walls. The path is shown projected on a face of area *ab*.

is brought into its final steady state chiefly by collisions between pairs of molecules; nevertheless, such collisions can be neglected when once the steady state has been reached. For, consider the set of molecules whose velocities are roughly equal, in magnitude and direction, to a particular value **c**. A steady state of the gas is such that the number of molecules of this set in any region does not vary as the time passes; that is, just as many molecules are deflected into the set by collisions with other molecules in any length of time as are deflected out of it. The molecules deflected into the set can be regarded as carrying on the motions of those deflected out, so that collisions between pairs of molecules produce no effect on the motions of molecules of the set, and similarly on the motions of all the molecules as an aggregate. Such collisions accordingly are neglected in calculating the pressure.

We first calculate the pressure in a very simple case. The vessel is supposed to be a rectangular box with edges a, b, and c, and its faces are supposed to reflect elastically the molecules which collide with them; that is, when a molecule strikes a face, its motion perpendicular to the face is reversed, and its motion parallel to the face is unaltered. Take co-ordinate axes Ox, Oy, and Oz along three edges of the box whose lengths are a, b, and c respectively. Then if a molecule initially has a velocity with components u, v, and w parallel to these axes, its velocity at any later time always has components $\pm u$, $\pm v$, and $\pm w$ (see Fig. 2). Let S be a face of the box, of area bc. Between two successive collisions with S the molecule has to travel a distance a perpendicular to S up to the opposite face, and a distance a back, moving all the time with speed u perpendicular to S. Thus the interval between successive collisions with S is $2a/u$, and the molecule strikes S $u/2a$ times per second. At each collision the molecule suffers a change in momentum of amount $2mu$, from $-mu$ to mu. Hence the total change in momentum of the molecule per second in its collisions with S is

$$2mu \times u/2a = mu^2/a.$$

Let n be the number of molecules per unit volume; then $nabc$ is the total number of molecules present. The total change in momentum at all their collisions with S per second is

$$nabc \times m\overline{u^2}/a = mn\,bc\,\overline{u^2}$$

where a bar over a symbol denotes that a mean value is to be taken. Now a pressure is a force per unit area, and a force is measured by the rate at which it changes momentum; hence, if p is the pressure of the gas, pbc is the rate at which momentum is being changed by collisions with S, or

$$p = mn\overline{u^2}.$$

Now, since no one direction of motion is preferred above another

$$\overline{u^2}=\overline{v^2}=\overline{w^2}=\tfrac{1}{3}\,(\overline{u^2+v^2+w^2})=\tfrac{1}{3}\,\overline{c^2},$$

c being the total speed of a molecule. Thus

$$p=\tfrac{1}{3}\,m\,n\,\overline{c^2}=\tfrac{1}{3}\,\rho\,\overline{c^2} \qquad . \qquad . \qquad . \qquad (3)$$

where ρ is the density (mass per unit volume) of the gas. Again, $\tfrac{1}{2}\,m\,\overline{c^2}$ is the mean kinetic energy of a molecule; thus (3) shows that the pressure equals two-thirds of the kinetic energy of the molecules in unit volume.

This result has been proved only by considering a special sort of containing vessel; but since experiment indicates that the pressure depends only on the state of the gas, and not on the vessel, the result should be true for any form of vessel. It can readily be seen that this is, in fact, the case.

First, the vessel need not be supposed to reflect elastically the molecules which collide with it. The number of molecules leaving the wall with a given speed in a given direction must be the same as if there were reflection, simply because the state of the gas is supposed to be one which gives no one direction preference over another. Thus the total momentum of molecules leaving the wall, and the pressure, is the same as if there were reflection. Experiment suggests that only a fraction of the molecules striking the wall are actually reflected elastically; some may become attached to the wall temporarily, and be later emitted in a direction, and with a speed, unrelated to that before reaching the wall. Equation (3) is valid in such a case just as much as if the walls reflect completely. A reflecting wall is merely the simplest sort which does not affect the isotropy of the gas—its lack of preference for any one direction of motion; in fact, a reflecting wall can be introduced anywhere in the gas without affecting its state.

This fact enables us to remove the restriction on the shape of the vessel. With a vessel of any shape, a small area S of the surface can be taken, which is roughly plane and square. On this as base, a cube can be constructed within the vessel, and the state of the gas inside the cube, and the pressure on S, are unaltered if reflecting walls are introduced along the other faces of the cube. Thus the pressure on S is given by (3), whatever the shape of the vessel.

Suppose that the vessel has volume V; then it contains N molecules, where $N = nV$. Thus

$$pV = \tfrac{1}{3} nVm\overline{c^2} = \tfrac{1}{3} Nm\overline{c^2} \qquad . \qquad . \qquad (4)$$

and the last expression is two-thirds of the total kinetic energy with which the N molecules move about. Equation (4) is equivalent to Boyle's law if the total kinetic energy is constant whenever the temperature is constant, i.e. if the motions of the molecules depend only on the temperature.

The pressure just calculated is the surface pressure—the pressure at the boundary of the gas. There is also an internal pressure, representing the action which the gas on one side of an internal surface exerts on the gas on the other side. Again remembering that force is measured by rate of change of momentum, the internal pressure can be seen to be the rate at which momentum is transported across unit area of the internal surface by molecules crossing the surface. Since the state of the gas is not altered by introducing a perfectly reflecting wall along this surface, the internal pressure is also the pressure which such a wall would exert on each side of it; like the surface pressure, it is given by equations (3) and (4).

The calculation of the pressure just given is simply the development of the idea first present in Hooke's mind. One may ask why Newton or one of the other powerful mathematicians of his day did not develop the calculation, and thereby jump straight to the point which science only laboriously reached by 1850. Indeed, if science were what it is often conceived to be, the work of great masters proceeding majestically by a predetermined plan to an inevitable goal, there would be real point in such a query. But the pathway of science is littered with discarded ideas—ideas which had to be worked out and tested before the true could be known from the false. In Hooke's day there was little by which the true could be distinguished from the false, and his idea was thought by most to be simply a speculation.

CHAPTER II

THE TRIUMPH OF THE ATOMIC THEORY

Phlogiston

WHEN scientists had finally discarded Aristotle's physics they had to seek new ideas to put in its place. Newton believed that matter was formed of atoms. As he put it, "It seems probable to me that God in the beginning formed matter in solid, massy, hard, impenetrable movable particles . . . so very hard as never to wear or break to pieces; no ordinary power being able to divide what God himself made one, in the first creation." We have already seen how Newton explained the pressure of a gas by the mutual repulsion of its atoms. His influence led many scientists to accept an atomic theory.

But the chemists were above such speculations, leaving them to natural philosophers who never entered a chemist's laboratory. Chemistry was felt by its devotees to possess mysteries all its own, and their speculations turned in different directions. Among the chief of their mysteries was fire, and its use in transmuting one substance into another. To explain this, a substance called phlogiston was invented. Phlogiston was supposed to be present in everything inflammable; when anything burned, its phlogiston was given off violently in the flame. The phlogiston could also be surrendered quietly, as when a metal rusts, or is turned into a powder by long heating. But if charcoal, an inflammable substance rich in phlogiston, were added to rust and the mixture heated, the phlogiston would re-enter the rust, and restore the original metal. The chemists of the eighteenth century regarded it as one of their chief tasks to study the mysteries of phlogiston.

Its properties were in truth mysteries. If wood is burnt, it loses weight; this was easy to explain, for it is lighter by the weight of the phlogiston given off. But if metals rust, the rust is heavier than the original amount of metal; how was this to be explained? By a chameleon-like change of properties, phlogiston had to become something which had levity—less than no weight—when it got into metals. And as time went on the properties of phlogiston became yet more remarkable and self-contradictory. As Lavoisier put it, "Sometimes this principle has weight, and sometimes it has not; sometimes it is free and sometimes it is fire combined with the earthy element; sometimes it passes through the pores of vessels and sometimes they are impervious to it." Yet for a hundred years it dominated the thoughts of chemists. Not until the end of the eighteenth century, when Lavoisier showed that burning was simply a chemical process in which the burnt substance combined with oxygen from the air, was phlogiston discarded.

But though phlogiston befogged chemists' interpretation of their work, it did not stop them working. The time was not wasted, even from the point of view of those interested in the atomic theory. Whereas chemistry was in far too rudimentary a state, in the days of Boyle, to supply proper experimental confirmation of his belief in atoms, the position was very different by the end of the eighteenth century.

Dalton's Theory

Atomic theory in its modern form is usually associated with the name of John Dalton, who in 1808 pointed out how simply chemical facts could be interpreted in terms of atoms. Let us see what the facts were which he had to interpret.

Boyle had given the first definition of chemical elements as substances which cannot be resolved into yet simpler substances, and from which, by chemical combination, more complex substances can be formed. Boyle did not assert confidently that such elements existed. In his day chemistry had not advanced far beyond alchemy, and the old alchemists believed that one substance could be transmuted into others; in particular, they believed that base metals could be transmuted into gold, if only the right way could be found. But in the eighteenth century it became clear that transmutation of metals was impossible by ordinary means, and the existence of elements was accepted as a fact. Several elements were isolated—metals, carbon, sulphur, phosphorus, oxygen, hydrogen, nitrogen, etc.

Chemists of the eighteenth century also recognized that there was a distinction between chemical compounds and mixtures. In mixtures, any proportions (within limits) of the mixing substances may be present; in a chemical compound, on the other hand, elements combine in definite proportions, though two particular elements may produce more than one compound by combining in different proportions. Again, the chemical properties of a mixture are those of the separate substances composing it; those of a compound are often very different. Thus, for example, carbon dioxide is a compound of carbon and oxygen, to form which three parts by weight of carbon always combine with eight parts by weight of oxygen; air is a mixture including nitrogen, oxygen, carbon dioxide and water vapour, the amount of water vapour varying from day to day, and the amount of carbon dioxide increasing at the expense of oxygen in a stuffy room. Again, air can support life because the oxygen in it does so; carbon dioxide cannot, its properties being different from those of the oxygen which it contains.

Not only was it found that elements forming a chemical compound have to combine in definite proportions; compounds joining in a chemical reaction likewise had to take part in definite proportions. Moreover, the proportions for different reactions were related; if, for example, x grams of one acid and y grams of a second neutralized equal weights of one alkali, they were also found to neutralize equal weights of another.

These were the facts which were becoming known to chemists when Dalton began his chemical work. He had worked for some time on meteorology and physics, and was a confirmed believer in atoms, thinking that Newton's work on gas pressures had shown gases to consist of atoms repelling each other. He therefore set out to interpret what chemical facts he found in terms of atoms.

First, he asserted that any pure substance consists of atoms identical in shape, size, weight, and every other particular. This was a new idea, even though Dalton believed that he was only following in Newton's footsteps. The ancient atomists had declared that the atoms were infinite in number and nearly infinitely various in form.

Next, he explained the difference between chemical elements and chemical compounds by supposing the atoms of the elements to be atoms in the ancient sense—indivisible particles—while each atom of a compound consisted of identical numbers of the atoms of elements, tightly bound together.

To those who objected to speaking of the ultimate particles of a compound as atoms, since they were not indivisible, he replied that they were indivisible so long as they remained particles of the compound; the compound ceased to exist as soon as they were split. The constant proportions (by weight) in which elements combine to produce a compound were explained by the identical composition of the compound atoms. Newton had, said Dalton, shown only that gases were composed of identical atoms; but since other bodies combined with atoms of gases in definite proportions, they must also consist of atoms.

Dalton made great use of symbols in explaining the structure of compound atoms. He denoted atoms of the elements by separate symbols, such as hydrogen ☉, nitrogen ⊕, oxygen ◯, carbon ●, and so on. Then he set out to represent compound atoms in terms of these; water was ☉◯, ammonia ☉⊕, carbonic acid ◯●◯, and so on. But here his representations showed him a striking fact. He knew of two compounds of oxygen and carbon, which he represented as ●◯ and ◯●◯; if his representations were correct, the weights of oxygen combining with a given weight of carbon in the two should be in the ratio 1 : 2. Similarly he knew of four oxides of nitrogen, which he represented as ⊕◯, ⊕◯⊕, ◯⊕◯, and $\frac{◯⊕◯}{⊕◯}$; the weights of oxygen in these, corresponding to a given weight of nitrogen, should be in the ratios 2 : 4 : 1 : 3. Here was a clear experimental test of his ideas. Without this, chemists might condemn his ideas as mere speculation—indeed, they were based on an altogether erroneous idea of what Newton had proved. But if experiment agreed with his theory, chemists would have to pay attention. His representations might not be correct, but even if they were not, whenever two elements combined to form more than one compound, the weights of the second element combining with a definite weight of the first must bear a simple ratio to each other, equal to the ratio of two small whole numbers.

Dalton set to work to show by experiment that this was indeed so. His experiments were not always very accurate, and he made some mistakes. But his results were sufficiently satisfactory to justify his publishing his ideas about atoms.

Scientifically, his methods were altogether wrong; he had his theory first, and then found the facts to fit it. But the essential was that the facts did fit it; whatever errors his reasoning might have involved, there must be something in the theory.

Other chemists at once recognized how beautifully Dalton's theory explained the chemical facts which they already knew. They repeated his experiments, and obtained results in general agreement with his ideas. They also realized that his theory predicted definite numerical relations in any chemical reaction; for example, if x grams of element A combine with y grams of element B or with z grams of element C, then, in any compound of B and C which may exist, y grams of B combine with pz/q grams of C, where p and q are whole numbers. Predictions like this were regularly borne out by the results of experiment, and so the theory came to be generally accepted. Some scientists, up to the end of the nineteenth century, were still careful to point out that the evidence for the existence of atoms was all indirect; no one had seen an atom. But, for all practical purposes, the existence of atoms came to be taken for granted.

Avogadro's Hypothesis

A further experimental law with a bearing on the atomic theory was also published in 1808. This was Gay-Lussac's law of volumes, which stated that, when two gases combine to produce a third substance, the volumes of the two, and of the third if gaseous, are in simple proportions; that is, their ratios equal the ratios of small whole numbers. Thus, for example, two volumes of hydrogen combine with one volume of oxygen to form water, and if the temperature of the apparatus is so high that the water remains vapour, two volumes of water vapour are produced. The different gases involved in any experiment are, of course, supposed to be at the same temperature and pressure when the volume is measured.

Dalton stoutly denied the validity of Gay-Lussac's law. He himself had tried to establish a law of this sort by supposing gas atoms of all kinds to be of the same size. His gas atoms were not the atoms of the modern picture—small bodies separated by wide empty spaces, and rushing about at great speeds. He supposed them to consist of a hard core sur-

rounded by an atmosphere of heat—most scientists of that day
thought that heat was a fluid—and the effective size of the
atoms was the size of the atmosphere. Each atmosphere was
supposed to press against others in its neighbourhood; the
atoms were not quite at rest, but moved only slowly from
point to point, and effectively the whole volume of the gas
was filled by the atoms. Thus, Dalton argued, if gas atoms
of all kinds have the same size, when nitrogen ⊕ and oxygen ◯
combine to produce nitric oxide ⊕◯, one measure of nitrogen
and one measure of oxygen should make one measure of
nitric oxide; in fact, they combined to produce nearly two
measures, and so different gas atoms must have different
sizes. Having decided this, he was not prepared to believe
that there was any relation between the sizes of different
sorts of atom, and attacked Gay-Lussac's experimental results
as inaccurate. He had made similar experiments, and his
results failed to agree exactly with Gay-Lussac's.

The inaccuracy, however, was Dalton's, not Gay-Lussac's.
There was, moreover, a fundamental oversight in Dalton's
reasoning. He had asserted that the ultimate particles of a
compound could be called atoms, since they were indivisible
so long as they remained particles of that compound; he did
not see that the ultimate particles of an element might similarly be compound atoms, indivisible so long as they remained
particles of the element, but splitting up into a number of more
elementary particles as soon as they took part in a chemical
reaction. This oversight was repaired by Avogadro in 1811,
in his celebrated hypothesis which fitted Gay-Lussac's law
into the framework of the atomic theory.

Avogadro did not speak of compound atoms; he called the
ultimate particles of any substance molecules. He asserted
that a molecule of an element, like that of a compound, may
consist of more than one atom, the atoms remaining together
until the molecule takes part in a chemical reaction, but then
dividing up. His explanation of Gay-Lussac's law was by
the hypothesis that equal volumes of different gases at the
same temperature and pressure contain equal numbers of
molecules. Thus, according to him, the volumes of gases
taking part in a chemical reaction were measures of the numbers of molecules involved. Dalton's picture of the reaction by

which hydrogen and oxygen combine to form water had been

$$\odot + \bigcirc \rightarrow \odot\bigcirc.$$

Avogadro, remembering that two volumes of hydrogen $\odot$ and one of oxygen $\bigcirc$ combine to produce two volumes of water vapour, would have pictured it by

$$\odot\odot + \bigcirc\bigcirc + \odot\odot \rightarrow \odot\bigcirc\odot + \odot\bigcirc\odot.$$

That is, he regarded molecules of hydrogen and oxygen each as diatomic.

Avogadro's hypothesis provided an explanation of the law of volumes, but went somewhat beyond this law; the law of volumes implied that the number of molecules of different gases in equal volumes were in simple proportions, but not that they were equal. Since Avogadro brought forward no new facts to support his hypothesis, it was disregarded for more than forty years. The chemical arguments which led to its final acceptance were far more advanced than those on which Avogadro could call, and cannot be given here. Here we are far more concerned with its interpretation. Had he accepted it, Dalton would have interpreted it as showing that molecules of all gases have exactly the same size. But he was thinking of gas molecules as pressed tightly together; we now know that they are widely separated. Let us see what interpretation is to be placed on Avogadro's hypothesis from the modern standpoint.

Theory and Avogadro's Hypothesis

In Chapter I the pressure p of a gas was shown to be $\frac{1}{3} mn\overline{c^2}$, where m is the mass of a molecule, c its speed, and n the number of molecules per unit volume. If Avogadro's hypothesis is correct, n is the same for all gases when p and the temperature T are the same. Hence the hypothesis implies that the mean kinetic energy $\frac{1}{2} m\overline{c^2}$ of molecules is the same for all gases at the same temperature. We can give a theoretical argument to show that this is so.

Kinetic energy is a concept first introduced into scientific thought by pure theory. Newton's second law of motion asserts that a force is measured by the change in motion

which it produces. A specified change in motion can be produced either by a large force acting for a short time or a
smaller force acting for a longer time; it is desirable to have
a measure of the total effect of a force in changing motion.
One convenient measure is the work done by the force—the
product of the force and the distance moved in its direction
by the body on which it acts. This equals the change in kinetic
energy $\frac{1}{2}mc^2$ (before the middle of last century usually called
the *vis viva*, or live energy).

Forces can be divided into two classes. One class, like
friction, always acts in such a way as to destroy motion, and
forces of this class are therefore called dissipative. The other
class, like gravity, can be used to store up work which can
later be released; for example, work done in lifting a weight
is given back by gravity when the weight is let fall. Work so
stored up, and available to be turned into kinetic energy, is
called potential energy. If no dissipative forces act, the total
mechanical energy—kinetic and potential—is constant.

The forces between gas molecules at collision cannot
include dissipative forces, since otherwise the total kinetic
energy would waste away, and with it the gas pressure, so
that, for example, a football would become deflated without
leaking. The effect of collisions between the molecules must be
simply to redistribute the energy among the molecules. If the
walls of the vessel enclosing the gas are perfectly reflecting,
the total energy of the molecules is constant.

Suppose first that a single gas molecule is present inside
the vessel. It moves about, and from time to time it bounces
off the walls. In special circumstances it may return to its
starting point, and repeat a finite path over and over again; for
example, a molecule in a cubical box can move to and fro
along a line perpendicular to two opposite faces of the box.
But only in special circumstances is this possible; its path
is infinitely more likely not to repeat itself, but to penetrate
in turn each part of the vessel. In the latter case, the molecule
spends just as much of its time in one small volume inside
the vessel as in any other equal small volume; we can say
that it is just as likely to be in the one volume as in the other.

Suppose next that the molecule is only one of a large
number of identical molecules in the vessel. The molecules

may now collide with each other, and so one molecule can repeat a path over and over again only if every other molecule does so too; this is so unlikely to occur that its possibility can be wholly neglected. This means that any one molecule in time ranges through the whole volume of the vessel; it is just as likely to be found in one part of the volume as in any other equal part.

As the molecule moved about, its velocity is continually changing. At first sight it appears natural to expect that, just as the molecule is as likely to be at one point as at another, it is as likely to possess one velocity as any other; but this is not so, since the total energy of the molecules cannot take any value whatever, but must equal a constant value. However, any one set of velocities of all the molecules giving the correct total energy can be shown to be just as likely as any other. The complete proof of this statement depends on advanced mathematics, and would be out of place in a book like this. We must therefore be content with the bald assertion that a proof does exist; the statement does, at least, appear reasonably credible even without an exact proof.

Let us see what consequences follow from the statement. Suppose, for example, that the energies of all save one of the molecules are known. Then the energy of the remaining molecule must be such as to make up the correct total energy, but the direction of its motion is not fixed. If one possible direction of motion gives energies E_1, E_2, E_3 to the motions parallel to the three co-ordinate axes, another possible direction gives energies E_2, E_1, E_3 to these motions, and the second direction is just as likely as the first. That is, it is just as likely that the molecule has x- and y-motions with energies E_2, E_1 as with energies E_1, E_2; in a long time, the one pair of motions occurs just as often as the other. Hence, averaging over a long time, the mean energies of x- and y-motion of a molecule are equal.

Again, by the same argument, the energies of x-motion of two molecules of the same gas are just as likely to be E_2 and E_1 as E_1 and E_2; hence, averaging over a long time, the mean energies of x-motion of the two molecules are equal. This result, like the one just derived, is in no way surprising; but far more important results can be proved similarly.

Suppose, for example, that two gases are mixed together in the same vessel. To compare the energies of molecules of the two gases, consider, in place of the true velocity c_2 of a molecule of the second gas, the reduced velocity

$$c'_2 = \sqrt{(m_2/m_1)}\, c_2,$$

where m_1 and m_2 are the masses of molecules of the two gases. The velocity c'_2 is such that the molecule of the second gas could be replaced by a molecule of the first gas with this velocity, without altering the total energy. Since all values of c_2 giving the correct total energy are equally possible, the same is true of c'_2. Thus, just as two molecules of mass m_1 are equally likely to have the velocities c_1, c'_2, or the same velocities interchanged, so two molecules of masses m_1 and m_2 are just as likely to have the true velocity c_1 and the reduced velocity c'_2 as the true velocity c'_2 and the reduced velocity c_1. Hence again, averaging over a long time, the mean energies of the two molecules are equal. In symbols,

$$\tfrac{1}{2}\, m_1 \overline{c_1^2} = \tfrac{1}{2}\, m_2 \overline{c_2^2} \qquad . \qquad . \qquad . \qquad (5)$$

the bars denoting that averages are to be taken over a long time, or, what is effectively the same thing, over all the many molecules of the two gases in the vessel.

Again, consider two gases not mixed together, but at the same temperature. There is only one way of ensuring that they have the same temperature, and this is to put them one on each side of a conducting wall, which lets heat pass from one to the other. The wall is to be regarded as itself composed of molecules, not rigidly fastened together, but held together by forces which, like connecting springs, let each of them vibrate to and fro. Molecules of the two gases strike the molecules of the wall and bounce off, sometimes faster, sometimes slower than they came, according as they receive energy from the wall or impart it. If a gas molecule imparts energy to a wall molecule, this passes it on to other wall molecules, just as the motion of a shunting engine is passed down a line of trucks, and the energy may finally be passed on to a gas molecule on the other side of the wall. Thus energy is continually being passed across the wall from one gas to the other.

The sharing of energy between molecules of the two gases is in no wise different from the sharing when the two gases are together in the same vessel; any one set of velocities of the molecules giving the correct total energy is just as probable as any other similar set. Thus molecules of two gases at the same temperature, like molecules of two gases mixed together, have the same mean energies. It follows that Avogadro's hypothesis is established as correct.

Equipartition: Dalton's Law

Theoretical proofs of the correctness of Avogadro's hypothesis were not possible at the time when the hypothesis was first stated; at that time the modern picture of the way gas molecules behave had not been clearly delineated. Such proofs had to wait until about the time that practical chemists came to accept the hypothesis for their own reasons.

As has been seen, the theoretical proof rests on the fact that molecules of different gases at the same temperature have the same average kinetic energy. This is a special case of a general principle, which we shall be meeting again later, called the Principle of Equipartition of Energy. Here the principle implies that there is a sort of communism between gas molecules; when they are able to communicate energy to each other they share out the energy among themselves in such a way that each, on an average, has as much as any other. The communism is not complete; a molecule continually gains or loses energy by colliding with others, and at any one instant it may have much more or less than the average amount. There is little in common with the political variety of communism, in which, ideally at least, each individual is given just as much as any other. This, like any other form of organization of society, embodies a conscious purpose, while molecular communism is the result of a series of accidental collisions. A more exact parallel is with the sort of communism that would exist in a primitive society, none of whose members cared in the least how much or how little they possessed.

The equality of molecular energies has only been proved for two distinct gases, but it clearly applies to any number. In particular, if a mixture of any number of gases is separated from a simple (pure) gas by a wall which transmits energy, the mean energy of molecules of any gas in the mixture is, when the gases have reached the same temperature, equal to the mean energy of molecules of the simple gas, and so is the same as the mean energy of molecules of any simple gas at the same temperature. The pressure of the gas-mixture is supplied by all the pushes exerted by its molecules on the walls, and so, by a generalization of the argument of Chapter I, it is given by

$$p = \tfrac{1}{3} n_1 m_1 \overline{c_1^2} + \tfrac{1}{3} n_2 m_2 \overline{c_2^2} + \ldots, \qquad (6)$$

where n_1, n_2, . . . are the numbers of molecules of the constituent gases per unit volume, m_1, m_2, ... are the masses of the molecules, and c_1, c_2, ... are their speeds. But $\tfrac{1}{2} m_1 \overline{c_1^2}$ equals the mean kinetic energy of molecules of the first constituent if it alone were present at the same temperature, and similarly for the other constituents. Thus the total pressure of the gas-mixture is the sum of the pressures $\tfrac{1}{3} n_1 m_1 \overline{c_1^2}$, $\tfrac{1}{3} n_2 m_2 \overline{c_2^2}$, ... which the constituent gases would exert if present separately, at the same temperature.

This result is known as Dalton's law of partial pressures; Dalton, whose first love was meteorology, proved it by experiments with water vapour in air. The law asserts that the pressure of each constituent in the gas-mixture is the same as if the others were not there. Dalton, believing as he did that gas pressures arise from the mutual repulsions of the molecules, took his law to mean that a molecule was only repelled by like molecules. As a consequence, he said, no amount of air pressure can stop water evaporating if the air is perfectly dry, but the evaporation at once stops when the right amount of water is present in the air—the vapour molecules pushing back any more molecules that might otherwise rise from the water. He was quite right in saying that evaporation can only be stopped by the presence of sufficient water vapour; he had the gift, common to all really great men, of being usually correct in his conclusions, even though led to them by unsound arguments.

CHAPTER III

THE HEAT OF A GAS

The Nature of Heat

ABOUT a hundred years ago a new idea began to permeate science—the idea of energy. Energy was something which could neither be destroyed nor created. It might take many forms; it might lie dormant, or be clearly manifest, but whatever vicissitudes it might undergo, its total amount was constant. It was not really a newcomer to science; various of its forms, like heat, and mechanical kinetic and potential energy, had long been known. The new thing was the recognition that all these were only different forms of the same entity.

Mechanical energy—kinetic plus potential—is indestructible so long as no dissipative forces are acting. This had long been known; but in no laboratory experiment can dissipative forces be wholly eliminated, and so this Principle of Conservation of (mechanical) Energy remained incomplete until it was possible to explain what happened to the mechanical energy when dissipative forces are present. It was first decisively shown about a hundred years ago that it is then turned into heat. Conversely, mechanical energy can often be supplied from heat, as when a railway engine is driven by power generated by boiling water.

Numerous theories of heat have been advanced in the past. Many early scientists thought heat must be a form of matter. Aristotle taught that fire was one of the four elements forming all matter; the ancient atomists believed that there were special atoms of fire; Dalton, like many others of his day, thought heat to be a fluid—"caloric"—forming a cushion round each atom. The modern view is that heat is simply energy of motion. All material is composed of extremely tiny particles—atoms and molecules; heat arises from the random motions of these particles. Thus the only difference between heat and visible motion is that in the latter all the particles are moving in the same direction at the same rate, like a well-drilled regiment on the parade ground; in heat motion, on the other hand, the particles are moving at random, like the same soldiers strolling around before the parade.

The modern view was first put forward in 1620 by Francis Bacon. He said: "Heat is a motion of expansion, not uniformly of the whole body together, but in the smaller parts of it, and at the same time checked, repelled, and beaten back, so that the body acquires a motion alternative, perpetually quivering, striving and irritated by repercussion, whence spring the fury of fire and heat." To put this into modern terms, molecules rush about, and are continually colliding with each other, or being pulled back by each other; the hotter the body, the faster are the molecules' random motions. Some of the arguments by which Bacon supported his belief now seem somewhat absurd; for example, he did not distinguish between heat and flame, and suggested that, when a candle is blown out by a draught, it is because the draught presses against the hot flame, and holds the moving parts of the flame still. Nevertheless, though his reasons were not all sound, his ideas were on the right lines.

Bacon himself pointed out that a nail hammered on the anvil becomes hot—the kinetic energy of the hammer turns into heat. Others following him amassed plenty of evidence of a connection between mechanical energy and heat. Boyle, in 1675, and Rumford a century later, pointed out that, in boring cannon, the mechanical work done generates great heat. Rumford managed to boil water, and Davy to melt ice, by heat generated by friction. The reader can easily multiply similar instances from his own experience. When a cycle tyre is pumped up, the work done makes the air, and so the pump, hot; when wood is sandpapered, it becomes hot; one can easily make a finger-tip unpleasantly hot by rubbing it vigorously on a sleeve for a few seconds; and so on.

Still, in spite of all this evidence that mechanical energy and heat were one, the idea that heat was a form of matter was not easily overthrown. Those who believed in caloric—heat as a fluid surrounding each atom—offered a different explanation of the facts. They said that caloric was a substance always trying to expand, but held round the atoms because attracted to them. When a body was heated, the extra caloric pushed the atoms further apart, and the body had to expand. When a body full of caloric was put next to one less full, caloric pushed its way from the first into the second, that is, the hotter body warmed the cooler. When heat was developed in boring cannon, or burnishing metal, the metal removed was supposed to lose part of its capacity for holding caloric, that which it could no longer hold coming out as heat. When gas became hot during compression, as in an air pump, caloric was supposed to be squeezed out of it by the compression.

It was nearly impossible to rebut arguments like these. Rumford showed, for example, that the metal shavings removed in boring guns had just about the same capacity for heat as solid metal, and argued that the heat of boring could not be caloric which the metal could not hold. But no one knew how much caloric the metal first held; if it held an enormous amount, the little that was squeezed out need not alter the properties of the metal much. The caloric theory could always be saved by extra assumptions, which could not be disproved.

But if the theory could not be decisively disproved, no more could decisive arguments be found in its favour. It was otherwise with the theory that heat and mechanical energy were one. If this were true, not only could an indefinitely large amount of heat be produced by expending sufficient mechanical work (as the earlier experiments suggested) but a definite amount of heat could always be produced by doing a definite amount of work. The experiments of Joule (1843–1850) showed this last to be the case. They settled the controversy: the caloric theory could give a general explanation of many facts, but it could not lead to definite predictions of this character.

In these days it is commonplace to speak of energy—energy of motion, heat energy, electric energy, atomic energy, and so on. But in Joule's day the word "energy" had hardly been given any technical meaning, and the idea of different forms of energy, each convertible into each other, was startlingly novel. Some measure of its novelty can be gauged from the extreme difficulty which Joule had in persuading British scientists of its truth. The British Association would hardly accord him a hearing, and only the deep interest in his work showed by William Thomson (afterwards Lord Kelvin) finally convinced them that his ideas at least deserved study. Continental scientists were perhaps a little less sceptical; indeed, some of them had in part anticipated Joule.

Solids, Liquids, and Gases

Joule's work suggested that gases were composed not simply of molecules, but of molecules in motion. Up to then the theory of gas pressures given in Chapter I had been regarded as highly speculative; but now it was recognized as much more securely based, and the way was open for a rapid advance in gas-theory. Actually, of course, Joule's experiments did not prove that heat is motion, but simply that heat can be generated from motion. He himself had no doubt that heat is motion, but more evidence was needed to prove this.

Clausius, a German scientist, amassed a large amount of such evidence by theoretical work. He pointed out, for example, that it is easy to explain why heat makes solids melt and liquids boil, if heat indeed is motion. A gas consists, according to the modern picture, of molecules rushing about through great empty spaces, and every now and then colliding with others. For most of its lifetime, a gas molecule lives by itself, with no interference from others. Solids and liquids are something like a thousand times as dense as gases, and so their molecules have much less chance of separate existences. Indeed, remembering how difficult it is to compress solids and liquids, we can expect that their molecules are tightly packed together. This does not mean that the molecules are hard solid bodies pressing against each other; it may be explained just as well by supposing that the molecules repel each other without actually touching. If two molecules repel each other very strongly when a short way apart, it takes an enormous force to push them together. That is, solids and liquids may appear incompressible, not because their volume is actually full of matter, but because the forces between the molecules hold them apart, and prevent any other molecules from slipping in. "Thus, a number of soldiers with firearms may occupy an extensive region to the exclusion of the enemy's armies, though the space filled by their bodies is small" (Clerk Maxwell).

The force between two molecules cannot be wholly repulsive. A solid resists extension as well as compression; a thin liquid film, such as a soap-bubble, tries to pull itself together and reduce its area, much as a stretched elastic sheet would. These and similar facts indicate that the molecules must attract each other at large distances and repel at small; when they are pulled apart the attractions come into play, and when they are pushed together the repulsions operate. A solid or a liquid is held together by the long-range attractions between the molecules. In a solid, each molecule is held in an invariable position by the attractions of the rest, and cannot change its neighbours; in a liquid, when circumstances permit, it can move between other molecules and find new neighbours, but it cannot wholly escape from the rest. This explains why solids are rigid and liquids are not.

Now, said Clausius, if heat is motion, the molecules of liquids and solids must be moving about, as well as those of gases. In a solid each molecule must have a complicated motion of vibration, always staying close to its average position, but darting towards other molecules, first on one side, then on another, being continually thrown back or pulled back by its neighbours. In a liquid the molecules still have a to-and-fro motion, and are pulled backwards and forwards by their neighbours; but their motions are not just vibrations, since they find their way about slowly from point to point. If a solid or liquid is heated, the to-and-fro movements of the molecules become more violent, and tend to push the molecules apart a little; this explains why solids and liquids expand a little when heated.

A molecule in a liquid moves about irregularly, and sometimes the pushes which other molecules give it may cause it to acquire many times its average speed. A molecule near the surface of the liquid, acquiring a large upward speed in this way, may be able to escape from the attractions of the other molecules, and wing its way into the space above the liquid. Molecules thus escaping are the cause of evaporation from the liquid.

Suppose that the space above the liquid is enclosed, and

at first empty. Molecules expelled from the liquid gradually fill up the empty space, and move about it like the molecules of a gas. In time, some of the molecules strike the liquid surface again; some of these may bounce off, but others are reabsorbed into the liquid. When this happens the vapour above the liquid is beginning to condense back into it. At last a steady state is reached when there are so many molecules in the space above the liquid that just as many molecules strike the liquid and are reabsorbed as are able to jump out of it. In this steady state, it is normally said that evaporation has stopped; but it would be more correct to say that both evaporation and condensation are always going on, and that in the steady state these balance.

The vapour in the steady state must have a definite pressure to stop evaporation. This vapour pressure increases with the temperature, since the faster the molecules move, the more can jump out of the liquid. An equal pressure exerted by some other gas would not stop evaporation from the liquid; the gas molecules would occupy only a small part of the space above the liquid, and so molecules jumping out of the liquid would find their upward passage unobstructed.

So far, evaporation has been supposed to occur only at the surface of a liquid. But suppose water is heated in a kettle. As its temperature rises, so does the pressure of water vapour required to stop further evaporation. Suppose a minute bubble of water vapour forms inside the liquid; such a bubble must be at atmospheric pressure. At first, atmospheric pressure is more than the pressure needed to stop evaporation, and so the vapour condenses and the bubble disappears. But when the water is hot enough atmospheric pressure ceases to be enough to stop evaporation, and the bubble grows. Hence ultimately, evaporation occurs by bubbles growing inside the water; when this happens, the water boils. Clearly the boiling point will be lower, the lower is the atmospheric pressure.

A similar explanation can be offered for the melting of a solid. When a solid is heated, its molecules move faster, and at last one or two of them are able to slip through their neighbours to new positions. At first these strays are immediately anchored in their new positions; but as the solid is further heated there comes a time when the molecules break away from their neighbours faster than new linkages can be formed, and the solid melts.

Pressure and Temperature

More direct evidence of a connection between heat and motion could be provided from a study of gases. The simplest evidence of this type was that provided by the theory of gas pressures given in Chapter I.

If p is the pressure of gas in a volume V, we found in Chapter I that pV is two-thirds of the kinetic energy of the molecules in the volume; thus Boyle's law implies that the total kinetic energy of the molecules is constant whenever the temperature is constant, and so depends only on the temperature. Again, in proving Avogadro's hypothesis in Chapter II, kinetic energy had to be supposed to pass freely from one gas to another whenever heat could also pass. This provides clear evidence of a close connection between kinetic energy and heat. Clausius himself could not appeal to the proof of Avogadro's hypothesis, for this was not given until some years later; but he could provide yet simpler evidence from the dependence of pressure on temperature.

Gay-Lussac, in 1802, pointed out that different gases, maintained at a constant pressure, increase their volumes in the same ratio when their temperatures are increased by the same amount. The increase in volume is roughly $\dfrac{1}{273}$ of the volume at 0°C. for each degree Centigrade that the temperature rises. This result had been discovered, in a rather inaccurate form, by Dalton about a year earlier; but, according to Gay-Lussac, the real discoverer of the law was Charles, who had known it some fifteen years before but had not been able to publish the results of his experiments. Charles's law is expressed in a convenient mathematical form by introducing the "absolute" temperature T, which is found by adding 273° to the temperature in degrees Centigrade. It then states that, when the pressure p is constant, the volume V of a gas is proportional to T. Since pV is proportional to the kinetic energy of the molecules the kinetic energy is itself proportional to T. Its dependence on the temperature again indicates that kinetic energy and heat are the same.

At o° on the absolute scale of temperature the molecules of a gas would have to have no energy. This fact explains why T is called the "absolute" temperature. More usual scales of temperature have zeros determined by the properties of special materials; o° Centigrade is the temperature of melting ice, and o° Fahrenheit was the lowest temperature which Fahrenheit could reach in his laboratory. But o° absolute is a temperature at which all materials must have the same property; none can have any kinetic energy which it can pass on to any other. For a gas can have no kinetic energy at this temperature[1]: and if it is placed in contact with a body which has energy to communicate to it, it will acquire energy and warm up; that is, the body with communicable energy must be at a higher temperature than the absolute zero. No body can have less energy than it has at the absolute zero, and so temperatures below the absolute zero are impossible. In fact, the absolute zero is itself an unattainable ideal state, though temperatures within a degree or so of it have been attained.

The average kinetic energy of gas molecules is proportional to the absolute temperature T; it does not depend on the gas considered, as was shown in Chapter II. We therefore write

$$\tfrac{1}{2} m\overline{c^2} = \tfrac{3}{2}kT \qquad . \qquad . \qquad . \qquad (7)$$

where k is a constant which has the same value for all gases, and so is called an absolute constant. It is usually known as Boltzmann's constant in view of the large share which the German scientist Boltzmann had in the proof of the Principle of Equi-partition of Energy. Using equation (7) in the relation

$$p = \tfrac{1}{3} mn\overline{c^2},$$

the pressure of a gas is found to be

$$p = nkT, \qquad . \qquad . \qquad . \qquad (8)$$

where n denotes, as before, the number of molecules per unit

[1] Actually all gases liquefy long before the absolute zero is reached. It is necessary, for the purpose of our argument, to imagine an "ideal" gas which never liquefies. Introducing such "ideal" substances is a favourite device in theory; but it is sometimes dangerous.

volume. If there are N molecules in a volume V, this becomes

$$pV = NkT. \qquad . \qquad . \qquad . \qquad (9)$$

Equation (9) embodies, as it should, Boyle's, Charles's and Avogadro's laws.

Molecular Speeds

In 1851 Joule pointed out that the mean speeds of gas molecules could be calculated directly from the equation

$$p = \tfrac{1}{3}\rho\overline{c^2}$$

since the pressure p and density ρ of a gas are both easy to measure. The equation gives the "root-mean-square" speed $\sqrt{(c^2)}$ of the molecules; this speed is not identical with the mean speed $\overline{c}$, but, as will be seen later, is about 1·086 times as large.

For example, the densities of hydrogen and nitrogen at N.T.P.[1] are about 0·00009 and 0·00125 grams per cubic cm. Since atmospheric pressure is a force of about a million dynes per square cm.,[2] the root-mean-square speed at 0°C. is about 1800 metres per second in hydrogen and about 500 metres per second in nitrogen. The speeds of air molecules are much the same as for nitrogen.

Such speeds are surprisingly large, implying, as they do, that our bodies are continually being bombarded by molecular pellets moving with the speed of rifle bullets, without our being in the least conscious of it. Still, a moment's reflection is enough to convince one that the speeds found are not only possible, but reasonable. A sound wave in a gas must travel from point to point because of the motions of the molecules, and so the speed of the soundwave cannot be greater than the mean speed of molecules. The speed of sound in air at N.T.P. is about 330 metres per second, about two-thirds the mean speed just found for nitrogen molecules. Thus molecular speeds of the sort of size just found are actually suggested by the speed of sound.

[1] A gas at atmospheric pressure and a temperature of 0°C. is said to be at N.T.P. (normal temperature and pressure).

[2] A dyne is the unit of force in the centimetre-gram-second system; it is the force required to give one gram an acceleration of one cm. per second per second.

The size of molecular speeds can also be checked experimentally by studying the rate at which a gas streams into a vacuum out of a small hole in the vessel containing it. The speed of streaming is found to be comparable with the calculated mean molecular speed $\bar{c}$, though smaller. The flow of the gas near the hole depends on other molecular properties as well as $\bar{c}$, and so the speed of outflow is not exactly proportional to $\bar{c}$ for different gases, though nearly so if the hole is very small and the gas pressure is low.

Measurement of flow through a small hole is difficult, and it is often more convenient to study the way gas seeps through a porous plug—a plug of a material like unglazed earthenware or plaster of paris, or even cotton-wool or blotting-paper. The seepage process is called transpiration. The rate at which transpiration ought to occur cannot be calculated by theory for any special gas, because the sizes of all the pores in the plug can hardly be determined: but the rates of transpiration of different gases can be compared. At low pressures, at least, different gases should flow through the plug, as through a small hole, at rates proportional to the corresponding values of $\bar{c}$. Since

$$\tfrac{1}{2}m\overline{c^2} = \tfrac{3}{2}kT$$

c is directly proportional to $\sqrt{T}$, and inversely to $\sqrt{m}$.

Inequalities of pressure on opposite sides of a porous plug can be set up by transpiration, even if the pressure is initially the same on the two sides. If, for example, a vessel closed with a porous plug is filled with hydrogen at atmospheric pressure, then, because molecules of hydrogen are much lighter than those of air, $\bar{c}$ is about four times as great for hydrogen as for air. Thus hydrogen seeps out through the plug far faster than air seeps in to take its place, so that the pressure in the vessel for a while becomes less than atmospheric.

Similar differences of pressure can be brought about by differences of temperature; if a porous plug separates two vessels containing the same gas at different temperatures, in a steady state the pressure is greater in the hotter vessel than in the cooler. If transpiration from one side is not impeded by molecules coming from the other, the flows from the two sides are proportional to the corresponding values of $\rho\bar{c}$, i.e. of p/c, or $p/\sqrt{T}$. Thus in the steady state $p/\sqrt{T}$ should have the same value on the two sides of the plug. Osborne Reynolds, in 1879, found that this actually was true at low pressures, when molecules travelling in opposite directions might be expected not to interfere with each other; his results provide direct evidence that $\bar{c}$ is proportional to $\sqrt{T}$.

Specific Heats

As Clausius and Joule both saw, yet further evidence can be invoked to show that the heat of gases is the kinetic energy of their molecules' random motion. The total kinetic energy can be estimated from the pressure; the heat of the gas can be measured directly; if the heat is really kinetic energy, these two quantities must tally.

Heat and kinetic energy are usually measured in different units; Joule's experiments showed that one unit of heat (calorie) is equivalent to J units of energy (ergs), where J is a constant known as Joule's mechanical equivalent of heat.[1] In this book, however, to avoid confusion, heat is measured in the same units (ergs) as kinetic energy; that is, a quantity of heat is measured by the amount of mechanical energy needed to produce it.

The amount of heat needed to make one gram of a substance hotter by $1\,°C.$ is called the specific heat of the substance. A gas has two specific heats. The first, c_v, is the specific heat when the volume of the gas is kept constant during the heating; in this case all the extra heat goes to increase the energy of the molecules. The second, c_p, is got by keeping the pressure constant during the heating; in this case the extra heat has to account not only for the increase in molecular energies but also for the work done by the pressure of the gas as it expands.

One gram of the gas contains N molecules, where $Nm = 1$. Thus if it is in a volume V,

$$pV = NkT = kT/m.$$

Suppose the gas is heated at constant pressure, and expands.

---

[1] A calorie is the heat required to raise the temperature of one gram of water by $1\,°C.$; the erg is the work done by a force of one dyne acting through one centimetre. A calorie is equivalent to about 42 million ergs.

If the expansion pushes a piston of area S back a small distance h, the pressure exerts a force pS on the piston, and this does work pSh. But Sh is the increase in the volume V; this we denote[1] by δV. If the corresponding increase in T is δT, then

$$p(V + \delta V) = k(T + \delta T)/m,$$

and so the work done by the pressure is

$$p\delta V = k\delta T/m.$$

The heat supplied to warm the gas, $c_p\,\delta T$, is the sum of this and the heat $c_v\,\delta T$ that would be required if the gas did no work. Thus

$$c_p = c_v + k/m \qquad . \qquad . \qquad . \qquad (10)$$

showing that the difference $c_p - c_v$ of the specific heats is inversely proportional to the molecular weight.

Often it is not the specific heat c_p or c_v which is determined experimentally, but the ratio c_p/c_v, which is denoted by γ. This ratio is determined from the speed of sound in the gas, which is $\sqrt{(\gamma p/\rho)}$. When it is known, from (10)

$$k/m = c_p - c_v = c_v(\gamma - 1) \qquad . \qquad . \qquad (11)$$

giving c_v; and c_p is γc_v.

If heat is the same as random kinetic energy, $\frac{3}{2}kT$ per molecule, the heat of the gram of gas is

$$N. \tfrac{3}{2}kT = \tfrac{3}{2}kT/m.$$

If T increases by $1°C.$, this increases by $\frac{3}{2}k/m$. Thus

$$c_v = \tfrac{3}{2}k/m, \quad \gamma = 1\tfrac{2}{3}.$$

When Joule and Clausius first made this calculation, no gas was known for which γ was as large as $1\frac{2}{3}$; γ was always found to be $1\frac{2}{5}$ or less, corresponding to c_v being $\frac{5}{2}k/m$ or more. Thus the heat of a gas could not be said to be simply the kinetic energy with which the molecules move about. On the other hand, such kinetic energy supplied an appreciable

[1] In mathematics, a small increase in a variable x is often denoted by δx. It is important to note that δx does not mean the product of δ and x; δx is to be understood to be a single symbol, measuring the increment in x.

part of the total heat, and it was not unreasonable to assume, as Clausius did, that the rest of the heat was mechanical energy of another sort. For example, several of the common gases, like oxygen, nitrogen and hydrogen, are diatomic; that is, a molecule of such a gas consists of two atoms fastened together, and may be pictured as a sort of dumb-bell, the heads of which are the atoms; or perhaps better (since all the mass is in the atoms, and they need not be rigidly connected) as two spheres fastened together by a stout spring. Molecules like this can rotate; indeed, practically every collision will set them turning. Again, if the two-sphere picture is reasonably correct, the two atoms of the molecule can vibrate to and fro, first approaching each other, then separating, and so on. Thus the molecule can have internal motions as well as those of translation bodily from point to point, and the energy of the internal motions can supply the rest of the heat.

Similar remarks apply to polyatomic gases, except that these may have several distinct sorts of internal vibration, and so should have bigger specific heats. On the other hand, gases whose molecules are single atoms may be expected to have no internal energy. When Joule and Clausius wrote, no such monatomic gases were known; the monatomic "inert" gases —helium, neon, argon, etc.—have since been discovered, and for these γ is, in fact, nearly equal to $1\frac{2}{3}$.

Suppose that, because of the internal motions, the average energy of a molecule is increased from $\frac{3}{2}kT$ to $\frac{1}{2}skT$, where s is independent of the temperature. Then c_v is increased to $\frac{1}{2}sk/m$, and

$$\gamma = 1 + 2/s \quad . \qquad . \qquad . \qquad (12),$$

For the common diatomic gases—hydrogen, nitrogen, oxygen carbon monoxide, nitric oxide—γ is nearly equal to $1\frac{2}{5}$, corresponding to s being about 5; the regularity of the values of s is challenging. Polyatomic gases show less regular values of s, the values being, however, always greater than 6. The increase of s with increasing molecular complexity is what is to be expected. It is found, however, that s as calculated from (12) is not actually independent of the temperature; it increases somewhat as the temperature rises.

Internal motions do not affect the pressure; indeed, none

of our earlier theory is invalidated because of neglecting them.

CHAPTER IV

THE FREE PATH: VISCOSITY

Molecular Collisions

WHEN Clausius joined those who believed that the pressure and heat of a gas were due to the movements of the molecules he met with opposition. Others suggested that, if molecules do actually fly rapidly about, two gases ought to mix with a similar rapidity. Actually a cloud, or a bank of smoke, often remains unchanged in form for a long time without mixing into the rest of the air. Again, if chlorine is released in one corner of a room, minutes can elapse before its acrid smell penetrates to the far corners, though the molecules of chlorine move fast enough to reach any part of the room in a tiny fraction of a second.

Clausius's reply to these objections was that the progress of molecules from point to point is not an uninterrupted flow through the rest of the gas; it is continually being interrupted by collisions with other molecules. In one sense, collisions happen only rarely; the distance which a molecule travels between two successive collisions—a distance known as a free path—is many times the size of a molecule. But a molecule itself is excessively tiny, and so the free path, too, is very small by ordinary standards. Consequently, when two gases mix, the molecules of one of the gases do not travel steadily into the other; they move in a zigzag fashion, first forward, then backward, then sideways, and though they do on the whole move forward their forward speed is far smaller than the random speed with which they are zigzagging about.

The rate at which gases mix is determined by the frequency of collisions between the molecules. Collisions between unlike molecules are the important ones; when, say, chlorine mixes into air, a collision between two chlorine atoms cannot seriously interfere with their joint progress through the air. In certain other processes, collisions between like molecules are also important. For example, a gas conducts heat because molecules moving from hot regions to cool carry more energy than those moving in the reverse direction; any sort of collision impedes the conduction. Processes like the mixing of gases, or conduction of heat, which take place because of the motion of molecules from point to point, are called free path, or transport, phenomena. Such phenomena will be the subject of this and the next two chapters.

First we need to calculate how often molecules collide with other molecules, both like and unlike. For definiteness, molecules will be regarded as rigid elastic spheres. This is not an exact representation; actual molecules need not be round, and they certainly do not strike against each other like hard bodies, but repel each other while still some way apart. However, a simple representation of a molecule is often very useful, even if artificial. If molecules are treated as hard spheres, the size of such spheres will represent roughly the closest distance to which two actual molecules can approach before the forces between them push them apart.

Suppose two gases are mixed together; let molecules of the two have radii r_1 and r_2, and masses m_1 and m_2. For brevity, the molecules of the two gases will be styled molecules m_1 and m_2 respectively. The numbers of molecules m_1 and m_2 per unit volume—in technical language, the *number-densities* of the two gases—are denoted by n_1 and n_2. We calculate first the number of collisions between unlike molecules per unit volume in a second.

Consider molecules m_1 moving in any special direction. Take two planes S, S' perpendicular to this direction, and a very small distance h apart. Those of the molecules considered which cross these planes have to travel the distance h between them, and run the risk of hitting molecules m_2 while doing so (see Fig. 3a). For simplicity, suppose for the moment that molecules m_2 are at rest, so that they can be treated as stationary targets which the moving molecules m_1 may hit. A collision takes place when the centre of a moving molecule is at a distance $r_1 + r_2$ from that of one of the target molecules. Thus, if the centre of each target molecule between S and S' is surrounded by a sphere of radius $r_1 + r_2$, the

D

condition that a moving molecule collides with one of the
targets between S and S' is that its centre moves along a
line cutting one of these spheres. Seen from the direction of
motion, each sphere looks like a circular target of area
$\pi(r_1 + r_2)^2$ (Fig. 3b); there are n_2h such targets per unit area
of the plane S, and so the targets appear to occupy a fraction
$\pi(r_1 + r_2)^2 n_2h$ of the plane's area. That is, a fraction

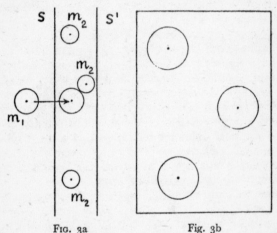

FIG. 3a   Fig. 3b

Illustrating the collisions of a molecule m_1 with
stationary molecules m_2 between two planes S and S'

$\pi(r_1 + r_2)^2 n_2h$ of the moving molecules hit targets while
travelling the distance h.

The argument does not depend on the direction in which
the molecules m_1 are moving, and so, of all the molecules m_1,
the same fraction $\pi(r_1 + r_2)^2 n_2h$ hit molecules m_2 while
travelling the very small distance h. While travelling a large
distance H, a molecule m_1 hits many molecules m_2; clearly
it must, on an average, hit $\pi(r_1 + r_2)^2 n_2 H$ of them. It travels
the distance H in the average time $H/\bar{c}_1$, where $\bar{c}_1$ is the mean
speed of molecules m_1. Thus the number of its collisions
per second is

$$\pi(r_1 + r_2)^2 n_2 H \div H/\bar{c}_1 = \pi (r_1 + r_2)^2 n_2 \bar{c}_1.$$

The total number of collisions between unlike molecules in

unit volume per second is this multiplied by the number n_1 of molecules m_1 per unit volume, i.e.

$$\pi \, (r_1 + r_2)^2 \, n_1 \, n_2 \, \bar{c_1}.$$

So far, molecules m_2 have been supposed to stand still, and act as targets. This assumption is roughly justified if they are much heavier than molecules m_1, as they then move much more sluggishly than these; but in general it is not valid. For example, the molecules m_1 might be the heavy, sluggish ones, in which case they would be the targets, not the strikers, and the number of collisions would be

$$\pi \, (r_1 + r_2)^2 \, n_1 \, n_2 \, \bar{c_2}.$$

In general, both $\bar{c_1}$ and $\bar{c_2}$ co-operate in causing collisions; it is reasonable to take the speed causing collisions as

$$\sqrt{(\bar{c_1}^2 + \bar{c_2}^2)}$$

and exact calculations show this to be correct. That is, the number of collisions between unlike molecules in unit volume per second is N_{12}, where

$$N_{12} = \pi \, (r_1 + r_2)^2 \, n_1 n_2 \, \sqrt{(\bar{c_1}^2 + \bar{c_2}^2)}. \qquad . \qquad (13)$$

The number of times a molecule m_1 strikes unlike molecules per second—the frequency of its collisions with unlike molecules—is N_{12}/n_1. The reciprocal of this gives the *collision-interval* τ_{12}; this is the mean time between successive collisions of a molecule m_1 with unlike molecules. Thus

$$1/\tau_{12} = \pi \, (r_1 + r_2)^2 \, n_2 \, \sqrt{(\bar{c_1}^2 + \bar{c_2}^2)}. \qquad . \qquad (14)$$

The mean interval τ_1 between successive collisions of a molecule m_1 with like molecules is got from this by replacing r_2, n_2 and $\bar{c_2}$ by r_1, n_1, and $\bar{c_1}$; the result is

$$1/\tau_1 = 4 \, \sqrt{2} \, \pi \, r_1^2 \, n_1 \, \bar{c_1}. \qquad . \qquad (15)$$

The Free Path

The mean free path l_{12} of a molecule m_1 between successive collisions with molecules m_2 is the mean distance travelled by a molecule m_1 in the collision-interval τ_{12}. Thus

$$l_{12} = \bar{c_1}\,\tau_{12} = \frac{\bar{c_1}}{\pi\,(r_1 + r_2)^2\,n_2\,\sqrt{(\bar{c_1}^2 + \bar{c_2}^2)}}$$

$$= \frac{1}{\pi\,(r_1 + r_2)^2\,n_2}\Big/\left(\frac{m_2}{m_1 + m_2}\right) \qquad . \qquad (16)$$

The distance l_{12} need not all be described in the same direction; it may be the sum of a set of straight paths interrupted by collisions with other molecules m_1. Similarly the mean free path l_1 of molecules m_1 between collisions with like molecules is $\bar{c_1}\,\tau_1$, i.e.

$$l_1 = \frac{1}{4\,\sqrt{2\pi r_1^2 n_1}} \qquad . \qquad . \qquad . \qquad (17)$$

The mean free path in a simple (pure) gas is given by a similar equation, i.e.

$$l = \frac{1}{4\,\sqrt{2\pi r^2 n}} \qquad . \qquad . \qquad . \qquad (18)$$

To interpret the last equation, we write it in the form

$$r/l = 3\sqrt{2} \times \tfrac{4}{3}\pi r^3 n.$$

In this, $\tfrac{4}{3}\pi r^3 n$ is the total volume of the n molecules in unit volume, i.e. the ratio of the actual volume of the molecules to the total volume occupied by the gas. The ratio r/l is about four times this quantity.

When water boils, its volume increases about 1700 times. Suppose that in liquid water the molecules are tightly jammed together; then the actual volume of the molecules is a little less than the total volume of the water. Hence, in steam, the actual volume of the molecules is rather less than $\frac{1}{1700}$ of the total volume. Similar results are got from the increases in volume when other liquids boil, and so it is not unreasonable to expect that, in most gases, the actual volume of the molecules is, at any rate, less than $\frac{1}{1000}$ of the total volume. Thus the mean free path is greater than 250 times the molecular radius.

Another way of putting this is as follows. Suppose that the total volume of the gas is K times that of the molecules. Then, since volumes are given by the cubes of corresponding lengths, the mean distance between a molecule and its nearest neighbours must be something like $K^{\frac{1}{3}}$ times the radius r of a molecule; if K is greater than 1000, this mean distance must be at least 10r. The ratio l/r being about $\frac{1}{4}K$, l is about $\frac{1}{4}K^{\frac{2}{3}}$ times the mean distance between neighbouring molecules. Thus if K is greater than 1000, a molecule slips past at least 25 others before at last finding one to strike.

So far, we can say nothing about the sizes of l and r separately, save that r is far too small for a molecule to be seen with the most powerful microscope. To estimate their actual sizes, we next consider one of the free-path phenomena in gases—the phenomenon of viscosity.

Viscosity

Viscosity is the stiffness which makes it difficult to pour or stir treacle. It is most apparent in treacly liquids, but it operates in any liquid or gas whenever one part flows past another. It is like an internal friction. When gas flows along a tube, the wall of the tube exerts a drag on the gas flowing near it; the slower gas near the walls of the tube similarly exerts a drag on the faster gas in the middle. In the same way, when a pendulum beats in air, the air through which it moves tends to make its swings die away.

Tait explained the way in which viscosity works in much the following manner. Suppose two very long trains of trucks are travelling side by side, the one rather faster than the other. Suppose that men in the trucks continually throw loaded sacks from each train to the other. Every time a sack from the faster train lands on the slower it is moving faster than the train it hits, and so gives the train a jolt, tending to make it move faster. Similarly every time a sack lands on the faster train, this train receives a jolt, tending to slow it down. The resultant effect is to tend to equalize the speeds of the trains.

When gas flows down a tube, gas flowing along the centre of the tube can be likened to the fast train, gas flowing nearer to the tube walls to the slower train. The sacks thrown from one train to the other represent the molecules moving in free paths outward from the centre of the tube, or inward to the centre. The molecules carry with them the momentum of the regions whence they come; thus molecules coming from the slowly moving gas tend to slow down the faster gas near the centre of the tube, while molecules moving away from the centre of the tube tend to speed up the surrounding gas.

To calculate the effect of the viscosity, suppose for simplicity that gas is flowing in a particular direction with a speed which is constant over each of a set of planes parallel to this direction, but varies from plane to plane. To fix one's ideas, the gas can be supposed to move horizontally, from left to right, with a speed W which increases with increasing height. Let A be any area in a horizontal plane, which molecules are

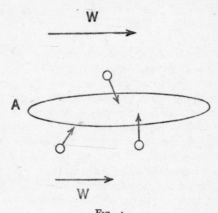

FIG. 4

Molecules transporting momentum across the horizontal area A

continually crossing upward and downward (Fig. 4). The faster gas above A tends to drag forward the slower gas below and the gas below tends to drag back the gas above with an equal force. Since force is measured by rate of change of momentum, the drag across A is given by the rate at which momentum in the direction of W crosses A because of molecules crossing from one side of A to the other.

Of all the molecules, n per unit volume, near A, $\frac{1}{2}n$ are rising, $\frac{1}{2}n$ descending. If all molecules had the same vertical speed u, the number rising across A per second would be $\frac{1}{2}nuA$; to allow for differences in vertical speeds, this must be replaced by $\frac{1}{2}n\bar{u}A$, where $\bar{u}$ is the average vertical velocity of all the rising molecules. It can be shown[1] that $\bar{u}$ is half the mean molecular speed $\bar{c}$; thus the number of molecules rising across A per second is $\frac{1}{4}n\bar{c}A$. The number sinking across A is, of course, the same.

The molecules rising across A come from a level some way below A; the exact level is hard to calculate, but it must be round about where they begin the free paths which carry them across A. Take it as at a distance al below A, where l is the mean free path, and a is a number which cannot be very large or very small compared with unity. Then the mean momentum of the rising molecules, in the direction from left to right, can be taken as mW_1, where W_1 is the value of the gas's speed W at a distance al below A. The total rate at which the rising molecules carry such momentum across A is

$$\frac{1}{4}n\bar{c}A \cdot mW_1 = \frac{1}{4}\rho\bar{c}AW_1.$$

Again, the rate at which descending molecules carry similar momentum down across A is

$$\frac{1}{4}\rho\bar{c}AW_2,$$

where W_2 is the value of W at a distance al above A. The net rate at which momentum is carried upward across A is

$$\frac{1}{4}\rho\bar{c}A\,(W_1 - W_2).$$

In this, $W_1 - W_2$ is, of course, negative; it is proportional to the very small distance $2al$ between the levels at which W_1 and W_2 are measured, and so can be put equal to $-2al\alpha$. The quantity α is equal to $\delta W/\delta h$, where δW is the change in the speed of flow on moving a small distance δh upward; α is called the rate of shear of small volumes of

---

[1] The result $\bar{u} = \frac{1}{2}\bar{c}$ is true if the motion of the gas as a whole is ignored compared with the enormously greater random motions of the separate molecules. Consider a set of rising molecules, all having the same speed c, but moving in different directions. If their velocities are represented by vectors OP drawn from a fixed point O, the points P lie on a hemisphere of radius c, with O as centre. The corresponding values of u are given by the perpendiculars from the points P on to the hemisphere's base; the mean value of u for a large number of such molecules is given by the perpendicular on to the base from the centroid (centre of gravity) of the hemisphere's surface, i.e. by half the radius, or $\frac{1}{2}c$. Thus $\bar{u} = \frac{1}{2}\bar{c}$.

gas past each other. In terms of it, the upward transport of momentum per second, or, what is the same thing, the force from left to right which gas below A exerts on gas above, is

$$- \tfrac{1}{2}\rho c \, . \, al \, A\alpha.$$

The minus sign, of course, simply represents the fact that the actual force exerted on the material above A is from right to left, not left to right.

The final result, then, is that the force across A per unit area is

$$- \mu \times \text{rate of shear } \alpha,$$

where

$$\mu = \tfrac{1}{2}a\rho l\bar{c}. \qquad . \qquad . \qquad . \qquad (19)$$

The quantity μ is called the *coefficient of viscosity* of the gas; it is this quantity which is determined by experiments on the resistance to gas flow. The constant a cannot be determined exactly by simple methods, and it was not until 1915—fifty years after the simple theory was first given—that Chapman at last determined it as equal to 0·998. Thus, very nearly,

$$\mu = \tfrac{1}{2}\rho l\bar{c}. \qquad . \qquad . \qquad . \qquad (20)$$

Molecular Sizes

In equation (20), the mean free path is, for any special gas, inversely proportional to the density ρ, and so the viscosity μ does not depend on the density. That is, a dense gas offers no more viscous resistance to a body moving through it than does a rarefied one. In the dense gas there are more molecules to carry momentum about, but each carries its momentum for a correspondingly shorter distance.

Maxwell, who first predicted this result by theory in 1860, was so surprised by it that he would not rest until he had been able to confirm it by experiments. Actually, however, Boyle had noticed much earlier that the swings of a pendulum die away through viscosity as rapidly in rarefied air as in dense air. Experiments since Maxwell's day have generally confirmed that the viscosity is independent of the density, save when the gas is so much compressed that the molecules fill a good part of the total volume, or when it is cooled so far that liquefaction is near to occurring.

This does not contradict the well-known fact that an aeroplane suffers less air resistance at great heights, where the air is rare, than close to the earth's surface. When a body moves rapidly through air, most of the resistance to its motion is not due to viscosity, but to the fact that the air is set moving in an irregular, zigzag fashion near the body. The degree of resistance depends now on the amount of air involved in the irregular motion, and is reduced by flying at great heights. Equally the resistance can be reduced by adjusting the shape of the plane's wing to keep the flow of the air as smooth as possible near it, and avoid irregularities of flow as far as possible; this is the "stream-lining" which is also employed to reduce resistance to fast trains and cars.

In measuring gas viscosity, irregular motion of the gas must be avoided. For this, either the motions involved must be fairly slow, or they must take place in a small space. Usually the resistance is measured when gas has to flow along a very thin tube. The measured resistance is not large; it is enough to check the motion of the gas, but then the gas has not much mass to be checked. The coefficient of viscosity is accordingly small; for most gases at ordinary temperatures it is between 0·0001 and 0·0002 units on the C.G.S. (centimetre-gram-second) scale. It is usually rather larger for heavy gases than for light, but the differences are not very large.

The measured value of the viscosity can be used to estimate how often collisions occur. For example, for hydrogen at N.T.P., μ is about 0·000085 ($8\cdot5 \times 10^{-5}$) units. Now $\mu = \frac{1}{2}\rho\bar{c}l$; also for hydrogen at N.T.P., ρ is 0·00009 grams per cubic cm., and $\bar{c}$ was found in Chapter III to be about 170,000 cm. per second; thus the free path l is about 0·000011 ($1\cdot1 \times 10^{-5}$) cm. The collision-interval τ is even tinier, because of the great speeds with which molecules rush about between collisions; since $l = \bar{c}\tau$, τ is found to be only 0·00000000000066 ($6\cdot6 \times 10^{-11}$) of a second. That is, each molecule undergoes fifteen thousand million collisions per second—truly living dangerously!

The radius r of a molecule has been estimated as less than $\frac{1}{250}$ of the free path; thus it cannot be more than one or two hundred-millionths of a cm. When molecular sizes were first estimated they could not be estimated more accurately than this, because of uncertainty about the number of molecules in a cubic centimetre of gas. This is now known fairly accurately, and, combined with the above values of l, indicates that the radius of a hydrogen molecule is only about 1·36 hundred-millionths of a cm. (1·36 × 10⁻⁸ cm.). Other gases have molecules with similar radii; the radii are never much smaller than that for hydrogen, or much more than twice as big. The radii are usually rather bigger for heavy molecules than for light, and for molecules of complicated structure (polyatomic molecules) than for simpler molecules.

Suppose that molecules in a solid or liquid are tightly jammed together; for simplicity suppose each molecule, of radius r, to be surrounded by a cube of side $2r$, and let these cubes fill the whole space without gaps. Then $1/(2r)$ of these cubes, side by side, fill up a centimetre, and the number of molecules in a cubic cm. is $1/(2r)^3$—say $1/(3·5 × 10⁻⁸)^3$, or 24,000 million million million. This indicates the sort of number of molecules in one cubic cm. of a liquid or solid; the number in a cubic cm. of a gas at N.T.P. (the same for all gases, by Avogadro's law) is about one-thousandth of this, the actual number being about 27 million million million (2·7 × 10¹⁹).

It is nearly impossible to think of numbers as large as these. For example, the number of gas molecules is so great that, if the molecules in a cubic centimetre of gas were shared among all the people on the earth, each person would receive more molecules than there would be persons receiving them. It is small wonder that, with so many molecules in the air, we cannot perceive them separately as they hurtle into us!

Slip at a Wall

The coefficient of viscosity measures the drag exerted on fast-moving gas by the slower gas which it is passing. The drag exerted by a solid body on gas flowing past it has still to be considered. A liquid flowing past an obstacle is usually supposed to suffer a drag because the liquid very close to the obstacle sticks to it. A gas, however, consists of many separate molecules, and so cannot stick fast to the walls of a tube through which it flows; even very close to the walls, it is slipping very slowly past them.

Suppose that gas streams steadily past a fixed plane horizontal wall. Let W_0 be the speed with which gas at the wall is slipping past it, and let a be the rate of shear near it. Then μa is the force per unit area which gas above any plane parallel to the wall exerts on gas below; that is, since the gas between such a plane and the wall is flowing steadily and so must, in the aggregate, be subject to no force, μa is the drag per unit area which the wall exerts on the gas flowing past it.

The experimental facts can best be explained by supposing that, of the molecules striking the wall, a fraction θ enter the material of the wall, and later leave it with velocities unrelated to those with which they struck it. The remaining fraction $1 - \theta$ are supposed to be reflected elastically. The quantity θ is called the accommodation coefficient; it depends on the nature of the wall's surface and on the gas, being quite small for a clean metal surface, and not much less than unity for a blackened surface. The fraction θ of the molecules have no momentum along the wall after leaving it; the fraction $1 - \theta$ have just the same momentum along the wall after hitting it as before. The drag μa of the wall on the gas is due to the momentum lost by the fraction θ.

The number of molecules hitting an area A of the wall per second is $\frac{1}{4}n\bar{c}A$. These molecules possess, on an average, the velocity of a level distant al from the wall; this differs from the velocity W_0 at the wall by ala. Thus the total momentum parallel to the wall carried up to the area A per second by molecules striking against it is

$$\frac{1}{4}n\bar{c}A \times m\,(W_0 + ala)$$
$$= \frac{1}{4}\rho\bar{c}AW_0 + \frac{1}{2}\mu Aa.$$

The drag μAa exerted by A on the gas is the momentum lost by a fraction θ of these molecules, and so

$$\mu Aa = \theta\,(\tfrac{1}{4}\rho A\bar{c}W_0 + \tfrac{1}{2}\mu Aa)$$

whence

$$W_0 = \frac{2\,(2 - \theta)\,\mu a}{\theta\rho\bar{c}}$$

Since $\mu = \frac{1}{2}a\rho\bar{c}l$, and a is roughly unity, this gives

$$W_0 = (2 - \theta)\,la/\theta. \qquad . \qquad . \qquad . \qquad (21)$$

That is, the velocity of slip of the gas at the wall equals the difference between the velocities of the gas at levels a distance $l(2 - \theta)/\theta$ apart. This distance is at most only a few times the free path. Nevertheless, the velocity of slip is important at low pressures, when l is larger than usual; it is also important in flow along a very fine tube, and so has to be taken into account in many of the more accurate determinations of the coefficient of viscosity.

CHAPTER V

HEAT CONDUCTION

The Conductivity

HEAT conduction occurs in a gas for much the same reason as explains its viscosity. Viscosity is due to the momentum which molecules carry from point to point, heat conduction to the energy which they transport. When a gas is left to itself, fast molecules travelling from the hotter parts tend to warm up the cooler gas, and the slower molecules from the latter cool down the hot gas.

Suppose, for simplicity, that the gas is at rest, and that its temperature T depends solely on the height. Let A again be an area in a horizontal plane. The number of molecules crossing A from below equals the number crossing from above; each of these numbers can be taken as $\frac{1}{4}n\bar{c}A$, just as if the temperature did not vary from point to point.

Suppose that the energy per molecule of the gas is $\frac{1}{2}skT$, so that (as was shown at the end of Chapter III) the specific heat c_v of the gas is $\frac{1}{2}sk/m$. Molecules rising across A come from a level some way below A, say at a distance bl below A, where l is the mean free path, and b a number which, like the a of last chapter, is neither very large nor very small compared with unity. Thus the mean energy of rising molecules is $\frac{1}{2}skT_1$, where T_1 is the temperature at a distance bl below A; the total energy carried by such molecules across A per second is

$$\tfrac{1}{4}n\bar{c}A \times \tfrac{1}{2}skT_1.$$

The energy carried by descending molecules across A per second similarly is

$$\tfrac{1}{4}n\bar{c}A \times \tfrac{1}{2}skT_2,$$

where T_2 is the temperature at a height bl above A. The net flow of energy upward across A is

$$\tfrac{1}{4}n\bar{c}A \times \tfrac{1}{2}sk\,(T_1 - T_2)$$
$$=\tfrac{1}{4}\,mn\bar{c}\,A\,c_v\,(T_1 - T_2).$$

The levels at which T_1 and T_2 are measured are very close together. The temperatures at two levels a very small distance δh apart differ by a very small quantity δT proportional to δh; the ratio $\delta T/\delta h$ is called the temperature gradient. Denote it by β; then $T_2 - T_1 = \beta \,.\, 2bl$, and the net rate of flow of energy upward across A is

$$- \tfrac{1}{2}mn\bar{c}Ac_v \,.\, bl\beta = - \tfrac{1}{2}b\rho l\bar{c}c_v A\beta.$$

The minus sign in this simply represents the fact that β is positive if the gas is hotter at high levels than at low, and in this case heat clearly travels down. The rate of flow of heat across A is put equal to $- \lambda A\beta$, where λ is called the heat conductivity; thus

$$\lambda = \tfrac{1}{2}b\rho l\bar{c}c_v. \qquad . \qquad . \qquad . \qquad (22)$$

This formula is reminiscent of the formula

$$\mu = \tfrac{1}{2}a\rho l\bar{c}$$

for the viscosity. Both formulae involve the product $l\bar{c}$, as is to be expected, since in both heat conduction and viscosity the molecules have to carry something through a free path l at a rate $\bar{c}$. The similarity between the formulae can be exhibited by writing

$$\lambda = f\mu c_v \qquad . \qquad . \qquad . \qquad . \qquad (23)$$

where $f = b/a$, and so f is a number neither much larger nor much less than unity.

One may well ask why the numbers b and a are not identical, since they arise from much the same kind of process. The reason is to be found in what happens when molecules collide. When one molecule strikes another, its forward motion is not altogether destroyed; part of the motion after the collision is unrelated to that before, but part of the previous motion survives. Especially is this true for fast molecules, which knock on their slower fellows, and themselves persist in moving forward with much of their previous energy. Thus molecules rising across a horizontal area must be regarded as originating, not at the level where they last collided, but at somewhat lower levels; that is, the energies and momenta which they carry across the area are those characteristic of these lower levels.

The question now arises, how much lower are these levels? A complete answer to this question would be very difficult to supply; but it is easy to see that the level for heat conduction is lower than that for viscosity. In viscosity, what concerns us is not simply whether a rising molecule goes on rising after collision; it must keep its horizontal momentum if the level from which it rises is to be counted as lower than the level of its collision. That is, the persistence of motion which interests us is a double one; both the vertical motion and the horizontal motion must persist after collision, and cases when both of these persist are relatively infrequent. For energy, on the other hand, a molecule which persists in moving upwards must carry most of its kinetic energy with it—at least so far as energy of translation is concerned; this is especially true of the fast molecules which carry most of the energy. It follows, then, that the persistence of motion is more important for heat conduction than for viscosity; consequently, of the two constants a and b, b is decidedly the larger.

Experimental Results

The equation

$$\lambda = f\mu c_v$$

is, on the face of it, ideally suited for providing an experimental test of a theory, for the quantities λ, μ and c_v are each directly determinable by experiment. Unfortunately, however, the thermal conductivity is very hard to determine. Hot gas always tends to rise; thus whenever experiments are carried out, in which one part of the gas is hotter than another, the gas tends to flow from place to place, and the flow carries far more heat than true conduction does. Only if the apparatus can be so arranged that currents are unlikely to be set up can one be sure that what is being measured is genuine heat conduction.

To help to ensure that currents will not flow, measures are often made at low pressures, since the forces that tend to provoke convection are proportional to the pressure, while viscosity, which tends to choke convection, is independent of the pressure. This in itself introduces a different difficulty, since there is a temperature-drop at a hot wall, very similar to the velocity of slip along a wall which was considered in the last chapter. The gas at a hot wall can be shown, by methods like those used in discussing the velocity of slip, to be cooler than the wall by

$$(2 - \theta)bl\beta/\theta,$$

i.e. the amount by which the temperature changes in a distance $(2 - \theta)bl/\theta$, which is a few times a free path. A thin hot wire is often used in measuring heat conduction; near such a wire the temperature may alter quite appreciably in a few free paths, especially at low pressures, when the free path is longer than usual.

When these difficulties have been overcome—and they have been finally overcome only in the last few years—the difficulty remains that theory has not been able to supply an exact value for f in all cases. Detailed theory shows that f is almost exactly 2·5 if the molecules have no internal energy; but the consideration of molecules with internal energy has daunted even the most stout-hearted mathematicians so far. A crude formula was, however, obtained by Eucken in 1913 as follows.

The total energy, $\frac{1}{2}skT$ per molecule, can be divided into two parts, the energy of translation, $\frac{3}{2}kT$ per molecule, and the internal energy, which is the remaining $\frac{1}{2}(s - 3)kT$. The ratio γ of specific heats of the gas is $1 + 2/s$; thus the energy of translation provides a fraction

$$\frac{3}{s} = \frac{3}{2}(\gamma - 1)$$

of the total heat, and internal energy the rest. In heat conduction, suppose these behave in an unrelated way; then each can be given a suitable value of f, f_1 for translatory energy, f_2 for internal, and

$$\lambda = f_1 \mu \cdot \tfrac{3}{2} (\gamma - 1) c_v + f_2 \mu \cdot (1 - \tfrac{3}{2} (\gamma - 1)) c_v.$$

Now f_1, which refers to translatory energy, may be taken to be 2·5, just as if there were no internal energy. Again, in considering internal energy, we have to take into account a persistence of motion after collisions very like that for viscosity; in viscosity we need both an upward motion and an unrelated horizontal motion to persist after collision, while in the transport of internal energy both the upward motion and an unrelated internal energy have to persist. If the transport of internal energy is supposed to be exactly like that of momentum, $f_2 = 1$. Hence

$$\lambda = \mu c_v \{ \tfrac{5}{2} \cdot \tfrac{3}{2} (\gamma - 1) + 1 - \tfrac{3}{2} (\gamma - 1) \}$$
$$= \tfrac{1}{4} (9 \gamma - 5) \mu c_v, \quad . \quad . \quad . \quad (24)$$

and this is Eucken's formula.

The formula fits observations fairly well for most gases. For the monatomic "inert" gases, whose molecules have no internal energy, the experimental value of $\lambda/\mu c_v$ is about 2·5, as it should be. The common diatomic gases give values of $\lambda/\mu c_v$ between 2·02 (for hydrogen) and 1·86 (for nitric oxide); the value of γ for such gases is about 1·4, which makes $\tfrac{1}{4} (9\gamma - 5)$ equal to 1·9. Some polyatomic gases also give a reasonably good agreement with the formula. But the agreement is by no means uniformly good, and suggests that Eucken's formula is too simple to represent all the facts.

Thus, up to the present, no exact equation for the heat conductivity has been given. Theory tells us roughly how a gas conducts heat, but not exactly. Because of this, and because the conductivity is so hard to measure accurately, experimental values of it can hardly be used to determine molecular radii.

The Radiometer

The reader may have seen, in an optician's shop-window, a device known as a radiometer. This consists of a glass vessel from which most of the air has been removed, inside which there is a sort of tiny mill. The mill consists of four vanes of metal foil, blackened on one side, each in a vertical plane, and fastened to a vertical wire which can turn about pivots at its upper and lower ends (Fig. 5). When the sun's rays fall on the mill, it turns rapidly; in especially sensitive forms of the device the heat of a candle or even of the hand is enough to make it turn.

Crookes, who first constructed the radiometer in 1873, gave it that name because he thought that its behaviour was due to the fact that the rays of heat falling on the blackened

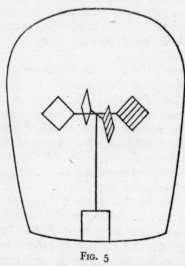

Fig. 5
The radiometer.

surfaces push them back. He did not believe that the air in the vessel could have any serious effect, since the mill did not work until nearly all the air had been removed. Nevertheless, it is the air which is really responsible for the turning. When the sun's rays fall on the mill, the black surfaces absorb more heat than the bright ones, which reflect better; thus the dark surfaces get slightly hotter than the bright. When molecules hit a hot surface, they tend to take its temperature, and so they leave it with greater speeds than those with which they approached it. Each molecule gives a sail of the mill a push

E

as it strikes it; the pushes are stronger on the hot side than on the cool, because molecules are thrown back faster from the hot side. Thus, on the whole, the molecules push the sails round, the bright sides of them leading.

At ordinary pressures the sails would not be pushed round. The fast molecules leaving the hot side of a sail push back the air near the sail, and so the air near the hot side is rather less dense than that in the rest of the vessel; this means that fewer molecules can hit the hot side, and this just balances the extra violence of the pushes which they give it. Otherwise expressed, the argument is that the sail warms up the air near it; the air pressure is the same at all points of the vessel, but it is exerted by fewer, though hotter, molecules near the hot side of the sail.

At low pressures the situation is altogether different. The free path becomes much greater, and may be bigger than the width of a sail. When this is so, molecules approaching a sail are no longer pushed back by the fast molecules leaving it; the free path during the course of which they hit the sail starts a relatively great way off—perhaps at the wall of the containing vessel itself—where conditions are not greatly affected by the temperature of the sail. Thus, surprising as it may seem, the molecules are able to push the sails round best when there are not too many of them. At very low pressures, of course, the molecules would be too few to exert much force; their effect is greatest when they are not too few, nor so many that they get in each other's way.

Suppose that molecules striking the sails come from such a distance that their temperature is not affected by that of the surface they hit. Take the pressure of air well away from the sails as p_o; let p_1 and p_2 be the pressures which the air would exert if everywhere at the temperature of the hot or cold face of a sail. The pressure exerted by a gas on a surface maintained at the same temperature as the gas is the sum of two equal parts, one due to the momentum which the molecules carry up to the surface, the other to that with which they leave it. The pressure of air on a sail consists of two similar parts; the first, due to momentum carried up to a sail, is unaffected by the difference in temperature between air and sail, and so is $\frac{1}{2}p_o$; the second, due to momentum carried away, would be $\frac{1}{2}p_1$ on the hotter face of a sail, and $\frac{1}{2}p_2$ on the cooler, if every molecule striking the sail acquired the temperature of the face struck. Actually, however, only fractions θ_1, θ_2 of the molecules striking the two faces take the temperatures of those faces, where θ_1, θ_2 are the accommodation coefficients of the faces. Thus the pressure due to molecules leaving a face becomes

$$\tfrac{1}{2}\left\{\theta_1 p_1 + (1 - \theta_1) p_0\right\}$$

for the hotter face, and

$$\tfrac{1}{2}\left\{\theta_2 p_2 + (1 - \theta_2) p_0\right\}$$

for the cooler; the difference between these pressures, which is

$$\tfrac{1}{2}\left\{\theta_1 p_1 - (\theta_1 - \theta_2) p_0 - \theta_2 p_2\right\}$$

is what is effective in driving the mill.

This expression is valid only at very low pressures. An expression valid when the pressure is not quite so low—when there is enough force to drive the mill, but molecules leaving the vanes interfere somewhat with those approaching—is very difficult to obtain.

CHAPTER VI

DIFFUSION

Mutual Diffusion

By diffusion is meant any process such that one gas flows through another in a mixture containing them both. Diffusion can occur for a number of reasons. First, it can happen as two gases mix into each other—as, for example, when appetizing smells of cooking penetrate throughout a house. Next, a force may act differently on two gases in a mixture; for example, gravity makes the heavy molecules in the atmosphere tend to move down through the rest, and to concentrate nearer the ground than these. Finally, heat acts rather differently on different gases; when part of a vessel containing a mixture of two gases is kept hotter than the rest the lighter gas tends to collect in the hotter regions.

Consider first the sort of diffusion which occurs as two gases mix. This can be likened to what might happen in a student "rag" of the kind in which opposing "armies" pelt each other with bags of flour and soot. Suppose that the bags are not designed to burst, but stay whole; suppose also that the throwers are scattered over the whole arena, and that, in the excess of their *joie de vivre*, they do not throw always in one direction, but impartially pelt anyone within reach with anything which comes to hand. At the start, we can imagine all the bags of flour on one side, all the soot on the other; bags of flour are not always thrown forward, but often come back; still, in the outcome, the bags of flour and soot will get thoroughly mixed.

The bags of flour and soot can be taken to represent molecules m_1 and m_2, belonging to two gases which are diffusing through each other in a mass of gas at rest. Throws of the bags correspond to free paths of the molecules. The analogy is not exact, since successive throws of the bags are unrelated in direction, but a molecule tends to retain part of its previous motion after a collision. Still, just as the bags of flour travel away from the side where they start, molecules m_1 tend, on the whole, to travel away from the region where they are initially most plentiful, and get thoroughly mixed with the molecules m_2.

Suppose now that the composition of the gas is constant over each of a set of parallel planes, but varies from plane to plane; as before, the planes are, for simplicity, supposed to be horizontal, but the effect of gravity is left out of account. Let A be an area in a horizontal plane. At a small distance δh above this plane, the number-density n_1—the number of molecules m_1 per unit volume—is $N_1 + \gamma \delta h$, where N_1 is the number-density on A, and γ here measures what is called the *concentration-gradient* ($\delta n_1 / \delta h$, where δn_1 is the increase in n_1 in the small height δh). The total pressure is the same at all heights, since the effect of gravity is being ignored; thus the same is true of the total number of molecules per unit volume, $n_1 + n_2$, and, if n_2 equals N_2 on A, it is $N_2 - \gamma \delta h$ at the distance δh above A.

If the composition of the gas did not vary with height, the number of molecules m_1 rising across A per second would be $\frac{1}{4} n_1 \bar{c}_1 A$, where $\bar{c}_1$ is the mean speed of molecules m_1. To allow for the variation of composition with height, this expression must be slightly modified. As in the last two chapters, the rising molecules have to be regarded as originating at a level round about where they began the free paths which carry them up to A, and so the n_1 in the expression $\frac{1}{4} n_1 \bar{c}_1 A$ is not the value on A, but that at a rather lower level. Collisions between pairs of molecules m_1 can hardly check the diffusion of molecules m_1 through molecules m_2, and so they are neglected. Thus n_1 must refer to a distance $d_1 l_{12}$ below A, where l_{12} is the mean free path of a molecule m_1 between successive collisions with molecules m_2, and d_1 is a number, like the a and b of the last two chapters, neither very large nor very small compared with unity. That is, the number of molecules m_1 rising across A per second is

$$\frac{1}{4} (N_1 - \gamma d_1 l_{12}) \bar{c}_1 A.$$

The number sinking across A per second is, in the same way,

$$\frac{1}{4} (N_1 + \gamma d_1 l_{12}) \bar{c}_1 A,$$

and the net number rising across A per second is the difference of these,

$$-\tfrac{1}{2} \gamma d_1 l_{12} \bar{c}_1 A. \qquad . \qquad . \qquad . \qquad (25)$$

The minus sign in this has a similar interpretation to that of similar signs earlier; γ is positive if molecules m_1 are more plentiful above A than below, and in this case such molecules diffuse downwards. The similar flow of molecules m_2 per second is given by

$$+ \tfrac{1}{2} \gamma d_2 l_{21} \bar{c}_2 A. \qquad . \qquad . \qquad . \qquad (25')$$

Here a difficulty arises. Since the pressure of the gas must remain uniform, the same is true of the total number of molecules $n_1 + n_2$ per unit volume; and this means that the number of molecules m_1 travelling upward across A must be balanced by an equal number of molecules m_2 travelling down. But the numbers (25) and (25') can hardly cancel each other out; l_{12} is proportional to $1/n_2$, and l_{21} to $1/n_1$. The balance between molecules rising and molecules sinking is only preserved by an additional motion of the gas as a whole. The flows (25) and (25′) lead to a minute difference in the pressures above and below A, and this in turn gives a vertical motion to the gas, sufficient to prevent any further pressure-difference from being created. Let the upward velocity so produced be V; then (25) and (25′) have to be replaced by

$$- \tfrac{1}{2} \gamma d_1 l_{12} \bar{c}_1 A + n_1 A V, \quad \tfrac{1}{2} \gamma d_2 l_{21} \bar{c}_2 A + n_2 A V.$$

If these two are to cancel out

$$-(- \tfrac{1}{2} \gamma d_1 l_{12} \bar{c}_1 A + n_1 A V) = \tfrac{1}{2} \gamma d_2 l_{21} \bar{c}_2 A + n_2 A V$$

giving

$$V = \frac{\gamma A}{2 (n_1 + n_2)} (d_1 l_{12} \bar{c}_1 - d_2 l_{21} \bar{c}_2)$$

Substituting this value of V, we find finally that the total number of molecules m_1 crossing A upward per second is $- \gamma A D_{12}$, where

$$D_{12} = \frac{(n_2 d_1 l_{12} \bar{c}_1 + n_1 d_2 l_{21} \bar{c}_2)}{2 (n_1 + n_2)} \qquad . \qquad . \qquad (26)$$

The number of molecules m_2 crossing A is equal and opposite to this. The quantity D_{12} is called the coefficient of mutual diffusion of the two gases in the mixture.

The formula for D_{12} is more complicated than that for the viscosity or the thermal conductivity. This is perfectly natural, for it applies to a mixture of two gases, not to a single gas. However, part of the complexity is more apparent than real. Since l_{12} is proportional to $1/n_2$, and l_{21} to $1/n_1$, the numerator of (26) does not depend on n_1 and n_2. Thus D_{12} is inversely proportional to $n_1 + n_2$, i.e. to the total pressure, and does not depend on the proportions in which the two gases are mixed. It is natural that D_{12} should vary inversely as the pressure; diffusion proceeds faster, the fewer are the molecules to obstruct it. The fact that D_{12} is independent of the composition is more surprising.[1]

[1] Actually, D_{12} is not quite independent of the composition; collisions between pairs of molecules m_1, or of molecules m_2, though they do not seriously impede diffusion, do so slightly. Accordingly equation (26) is not quite accurate, though adequate for most purposes.

Equation (26) shows that diffusion, like viscosity, depends on the product of a mean free path and a mean molecular speed. To indicate the resemblance more clearly, suppose that molecules m_1 and molecules m_2 are identical, so that the process being considered is diffusion of certain molecules of a pure gas through the rest. Imagine, say, that some molecules in the pure gas are painted red, the rest blue; the diffusion considered is that of the red molecules through the blue. The process is called self-diffusion; the corresponding diffusion coefficient is written D_{11}.

In (26), l_{12} is the free path of a molecule m_1 when supposed to be obstructed only by the n_2 molecules m_2 per unit volume; if it were similarly obstructed by all the $n_1 + n_2$ molecules present the free path would be $n_2 l_{12}/(n_1 + n_2)$. Thus, in the simple gas now being considered $n_2 l_{12}/(n_1 + n_2)$ gives the ordinary mean free path l; similarly, so does $n_1 l_{21}/(n_1 + n_2)$. Putting also $d_1 = d_2 = d$, $\overline{c_1} = \overline{c_2} = \overline{c}$, (26) becomes

$$D_{11} = dl\overline{c}.$$

Since the viscosity μ is given by $\mu = \frac{1}{2} a \rho l \overline{c}$,

$$D_{11} = j\mu/\rho \quad . \quad . \quad . \quad . \quad (27)$$

where $j = 2d/a$. Exact theory shows that j is about 1·2.

Experimental Results

Coefficients of mutual diffusion of gases are determined experimentally by letting the gases diffuse through each other along a tube connecting reservoirs containing either the two pure gases, or mixtures of the two in different proportions. The diffusion of a vapour through a gas is studied by letting the liquid which gives rise to the vapour evaporate into the gas. Just above the liquid surface the gas is saturated —as full of vapour as it can be—and further vapour can rise from the liquid only as fast as diffusion carries away the vapour from just above the surface.

Experiments on diffusion are not too easy to carry out. Diffusion is a relatively slow process, and, if the gases are stirred up at all, they mix together far faster than diffusion can make them. This is why a hot cup of tea cools far faster out-of-doors, on a picnic, than indoors; the breeze carries away the saturated air just above the tea, and so speeds up evaporation enormously. In the same way, in war a gas attack by a choking gas was less to be feared in wind, when the gas rapidly became stirred into the atmosphere and became diluted, than in calm air, when diffusion alone had to dissipate the gas cloud. In diffusion experiments, all stirring and currents in the gas must be avoided. Because of this difficulty, and because, in practical problems, mixing by diffusion is not the important process, experiments on diffusion have been rather few.

Consider first self-diffusion. It is of course impossible to follow the diffusion of specially selected molecules of a gas through the rest if there is nothing to distinguish them from the others. But it is possible to study the diffusion of a gas through a nearly identical one, and this is very like self-diffusion. For example, nitrogen and carbon monoxide have very similar molecules; each gas is diatomic, and the two have roughly the same molecular weight, specific heat, viscosity and thermal conductivity. The diffusion of nitrogen through carbon monoxide should therefore resemble self-diffusion. Carbon dioxide and nitrous oxide are another pair of very similar gases, each with triatomic molecules. Again, hydrogen can exist in two forms, called ortho- and para-hydrogen; molecules can change from one form to the other, but the change takes a matter of weeks in ordinary laboratory conditions. Thus a diffusion experiment is possible, very like self-diffusion, in which ortho-hydrogen diffuses through para-hydrogen. Finally, quite ordinary gases can be made slightly radioactive for short times, and the diffusion of the radioactive molecules through the others can be studied.

The equation

$$D_{11} = j\mu/\rho = 1\cdot 2\mu/\rho$$

is another of the equations ideally suited for an experimental test of theory, since it involves only directly measurable quantities. Experimental results do not confirm the accuracy of the equation; they indicate that j is about $1\cdot 4$ for the gases studied, not $1\cdot 2$. The reason is simply that, for the purposes of theory, the molecules have been supposed to be rigid elastic spheres, and this assumption is not good enough. If the molecules were taken to be softer, larger theoretical values of j would be got.

If determined to treat the molecules as rigid elastic spheres, one could explain the increased value of j by supposing that the free path is bigger for diffusion than viscosity; that is, that the radius of a molecule—which is, after all, a rather artificial and indeterminate concept—has to be taken smaller for diffusion than for viscosity. Precisely the same device has to be introduced when mutual diffusion is considered. In the formula

$$D_{12} = \frac{n_2 d_1 l_{12} \bar{c_1} + n_1 d_2 l_{21} c_2}{2 (n_1 + n_2)}$$

exact theory shows that d_1, d_2 are each about o·6; also

$$\frac{n_2 l_{12}}{\bar{c_1}} = \frac{n_1 l_{21}}{\bar{c_2}} = \frac{1}{\pi (r_1 + r_2)^2 \sqrt{(\bar{c_1}^2 + \bar{c_2}^2)}}$$

(cf. Chapter IV, equation (16)). Thus, roughly

$$D_{12} = \frac{\text{o·6} \sqrt{(\bar{c_1}^2 + \bar{c_2}^2)}}{2 \pi (r_1 + r_2)^2 (n_1 + n_2)}$$

If D_{12} is known from experiment, this equation can be used to calculate $r_1 + r_2$, the sum of the radii of molecules of the diffusing gases. The values of $r_1 + r_2$ turn out regularly to be 10 per cent or so less than the values calculated from viscosity.

Such a discrepancy is not disconcerting, nor even surprising. If the radii calculated from diffusion had turned out to be ten or a hundred times as big as those from viscosity—and, seeing that the viscosity radii were only one or two hundred-millionths of a centimetre, there is ample room for such a difference—the assumptions underlying gas-theory would be definitely disproved. But when, with an enormous range of sizes from which to choose, the radii turn out to be only 10 per cent different, clearly the theory is on the right general lines. Even the assumption that the molecules can be treated as rigid elastic spheres, though obviously not fully adequate, cannot be too bad.

Forced Diffusion

Consider now the sort of diffusion that results from forces acting on the molecules. To fix one's ideas, consider vertical diffusion under gravity; other sorts of forced diffusion can be treated very similarly.

Here a difficulty at once confronts us. Under gravity, any one molecule has a constant downward acceleration, and so tends to descend. Collisions with other molecules may impede its descent, but cannot altogether stop it; the molecules which it hits are not all moving upwards, but are themselves being impelled downwards by gravity. Hence every molecule in the gas tends to descend. Why then can the gas stay up at all; why does the atmosphere not simply collapse?

To answer this question, it is best for the moment completely to ignore collisions between the molecules. The atmosphere could not stay up against gravity without being supported by the earth's surface. Molecules are continually striking against this surface, and leaving it with mean speeds appropriate to the surface's temperature. The mean speed $\bar{c}$ of air molecules at o°C. is about 440 metres per second; a molecule leaving the surface with this speed vertically upward could reach a height of about 10 km. against gravity. This is only an average speed; some molecules leave the surface with smaller speeds than this, a few with much greater speeds; some travel nearly vertically, some in more nearly horizontal directions.

Thus a large proportion of the molecules cannot reach a height of 10 km.; a few of them reach much greater heights. At any time there are at any height some molecules rising, some falling, and some near the tops of their paths and moving nearly horizontally. The atmosphere as a whole has no mean velocity at any height, even though each molecule has an acceleration tending to make it fall. The effect of the acceleration is simply that there are fewer molecules at great heights than near the earth's surface.

Collisions between the molecules do not greatly modify this picture. Instead of themselves being able to rise to great heights, molecules leaving the earth's surface push up other molecules, and these push up yet others above them and so on; the molecules which they push against continue their upward paths.

If the temperature of the atmosphere were the same at all heights, then, corresponding to every molecule with velocity **c** which undergoes a collision at a particular level, there is a second which leaves a collision at that level with the same velocity **c**. The second is, so to speak, the inheritor of the first's motion; a molecule leaving the earth's surface, and the successive inheritors of its motion, between them travel along the path which the first would take if there were no collisions. The situation is a little more complicated if the temperature varies with the height, since then the inheritors of a molecule's motion must be supposed to have a speed rather different from that which the original molecule would have if it reached their level; but the atmosphere is still held up by the speeds with which molecules leave the earth.

In an atmosphere consisting of two gases under gravity, two sorts of diffusion occur. The first is a diffusion of the type considered earlier, tending to make the gases mix; the second is the effect of gravity, tending to make the heavier molecules sink below the lighter. A steady state is possible, in which the two sorts of diffusion cancel out. This steady state is not affected by collisions between pairs of molecules of different gases. One gas cannot, so to speak, be carried on the back of the other; if it has a natural tendency to sink through the other, it will do so, and will not be prevented from so doing by the presence of the other. Each gas must support itself; in the steady state the density of each must vary just as if the other were absent.

Suppose that in the steady state the first gas has a concentration-gradient $-\gamma_1$; that is, that between the heights h and $h + \delta h$ its number-density n_1 falls off by $\gamma_1 \delta h$. Then the pressure exerted by its molecules is greater by $kT\gamma_1\delta h$ at the height h than at the height $h + \delta h$. The excess pressure serves to support the weight of molecules m_1 between these levels; this is $n_1 m_1 g \delta h$ per unit horizontal area, where g is the acceleration of gravity. Thus in the steady state,

$$kT\gamma_1 = n_1 m_1 g.$$

Thinking of the steady state as a state in which the upward

diffusion due to concentration just balances downward diffusion due to gravity, gravity is seen to produce just the same diffusion as a concentration gradient $m_1 n_1 g/kT$. The rate of diffusion due to gravity does not depend on whether the gas is in the steady state or not; thus, if the state were not steady, the molecules m_1 crossing a horizontal area A per second would be the difference between $D_{12}\gamma_1 A$ travelling up, because of the concentration gradient, and

$$D_{12}A m_1 n_1 g/kT$$

travelling down, because of gravity. The last expression can also be written

$$D_{12}A\rho_1 g/kT.$$

The result can be generalized to apply to other forces. A force X_1 acting on the molecules m_1, in a gas which is, as a whole, at rest, makes such molecules cross an area A perpendicular to the force at a rate

$$D_{12}A n_1 X_1/kT.$$

This implies that the speed with which molecules m_1 are made to diffuse through the whole gas is

$$D_{12}X_1/kT. \qquad . \qquad . \qquad . \qquad (28)$$

One of the most important forces that can act on the molecules is an electric force. Such forces will be considered in detail in Chapter XII.

Thermal Diffusion

Suppose two vessels connected by a tube are filled with a mixture of two gases, one heavy and one light, like hydrogen and nitrogen. Let the vessels be maintained at different temperatures, say by immersing one in boiling water, and surrounding the other by melting ice. Then what is known as thermal diffusion takes place in the mixture; the light gas tends to flow towards the hotter vessel, the heavy one towards the cooler. The diffusion goes on until the reverse diffusion, due to the resulting difference of gas composition between the two vessels, is just enough to balance it. In the steady state thus reached, the difference in composition between the two vessels is not large. For example, if the mixture was originally composed of equal volumes of hydrogen and nitrogen, and the temperatures of the two vessels were 0°C. and 100°C., hydrogen would be, in the steady state, about 2 per cent more of the whole in the hot vessel than in the cool.

Thermal diffusion is a complicated phenomenon; no really simple theory of it can be given. In consequence, the early masters of gas-theory—Clausius, Maxwell and Boltzmann—were unaware of it. It was first discovered theoretically by Enskog in Sweden, and independently by Chapman in this country, about the time of the First World War; experimental confirmation of its reality came later.

The diffusion arises because of the difference between the ways in which collisions affect slow and fast molecules. A slow molecule is a nearly stationary target for other molecules to hit, and so the collision-interval for a slow molecule does not depend greatly on its speed. A fast molecule, on the other hand, hits others much as if they were stationary; its collision-interval is roughly inversely proportional to its speed. Thus fast molecules undergo collisions more frequently than slow; they suffer from a sort of handicap to compensate for their speed, and do not diffuse through the rest as fast as their speed would lead one to expect. In a mixture of a light gas and a heavy one, the light ones have an especially big handicap in their collisions with the heavy ones; even the fastest of the heavy molecules move slowly compared with the light ones, and suffer no handicap, but the light molecules are all more or less fast.

Heat conduction occurs in a gas because molecules from the hot parts are faster than those from the cool. According to what has just been said, fast molecules of a light gas are handicapped, compared with those of a heavy, as they attempt to move about in a mixture of the two gases. Thus light molecules tend to find it harder to leave a hot region than to enter it; heavy molecules experience no such difficulty. The outcome is thermal diffusion, the light gas tending to move into hotter regions, and the heavy into cooler regions.

Consider the steady state reached at the end of a thermal diffusion experiment, in which thermal diffusion is just balanced by the reverse diffusion due to difference of gas composition. In the cool vessel, of temperature T, let the proportions of the two gases be r and $1 - r$ by volume; in the hot vessel let the temperature be $T + \delta T$ and the proportions of the gases be $r + \delta r$ and $1 - r - \delta r$. If δT is fairly small, the rate of thermal diffusion must be proportional to δT; the reverse diffusion, on the other hand, must be proportional to the difference δr of gas composition between the two vessels. In the steady state, therefore, δr is proportional to δT; we write

$$\delta r = k_T \, \delta T / T. \qquad . \qquad . \qquad . \qquad (29)$$

Thus k_T is a pure number, measuring the ratio of strengths of thermal diffusion and the diffusion due to differences of composition; it is called the thermal diffusion ratio.

We shall not try to obtain a mathematical formula for k_T; the rather vague argument given above to explain how thermal diffusion arises is one which it is very difficult to translate into exact mathematical form. However, the general behaviour of k_T can be inferred without detailed work. If one of the gases is present only in small proportions, thermal diffusion makes this gas only a little more abundant in the one vessel than in the other, and δr, the difference in composition between the vessels, must be very small. Hence k_T becomes small when either of the gases is present in small proportions.

Thermal diffusion is therefore not much use in removing traces of an impurity from a gas; it is rather more use in enriching a mixture in some constituent of which it already possesses a fair proportion, though even in this respect its use is limited, because of the small size of k_T. In fact, during the last war thermal and other forms of diffusion were considered as possible means of separating out rare gases which were to be used in constructing the atomic bomb, but they were discarded in favour of other, more effective, methods.

The variation of k_T with composition is illustrated in Fig. 6 for mixtures of hydrogen and nitrogen; its variation for other mixtures is usually very similar. The maximum value of k_T depends very much on the pair of gases concerned. Since thermal diffusion arises from the difference in behaviour of light and heavy molecules at collision, it is not surprising to find that k_T is least for gases whose molecules are nearly equal in size and mass, and greatest when the gases concerned are very different. But this does not cover all the facts; even when allowance is made for differences of mass and size, some gas-mixtures seem to give values of k_T which are disproportionately small. It is suggestive that these mixtures refer to gases whose molecules are known not to be well represented by elastic spheres.

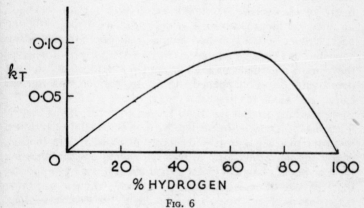

Fig. 6

Graph showing the variation with composition of the thermal diffusion ratio, k_T, in mixtures of hydrogen and nitrogen.

There is a process inverse to thermal diffusion. Differences of temperature have been seen to cause diffusion; on the other hand diffusion can produce differences of temperature. In an experiment carried out in 1946 by Waldmann, two different gases at the same temperature were made to flow slowly along tubes which were side by side, and connected with each other through a slit along their lengths. Gas was able to diffuse from one tube to the other through the slit; in consequence, gas leaving one tube was found to be very slightly warmer than that leaving the other.

CHAPTER VII

THE OUTSIDES OF GAS MOLECULES

Molecular Models

RONTGEN, the discoverer of X-rays, was not the first to have had the opportunity of making their discovery. He discovered them by finding that an X-ray tube could produce many of the results of visible light, even though enclosed in thick cardboard, through which ordinary light could not pass. Others before him had noticed that photographic plates kept in a box became fogged if left near the tube. But whereas they simply regarded this as an unwanted nuisance, and did not investigate why it happened, he set to work to find out the cause, and made his great discovery.

Something similar has been known to occur in gas-theory. The theory described in earlier chapters was mainly developed to prove that a gas consisted simply of molecules in motion. Many simple results were proved by leaving out complicating factors. Boyle's law was given a theoretical proof by supposing that the size of molecules can be ignored; if their size were taken into account, Boyle's law would not be exactly verified. If molecules are elastic spheres, the viscosity of a gas is proportional to the mean molecular speed, and so to the square root of the temperature; but since actual molecules are not elastic spheres this result, too, cannot be expected to agree with experiment. In the formula for self-diffusion

$$D_{11} = j\mu/\rho$$

the constant j must be 1·2 if the molecules are elastic spheres; but because they are not, j is larger for actual gases. In all these cases, a beautiful theoretical argument is marred by an unwanted intrusion, just as the photographic plates were marred by the X-rays. But if the intrusions are further investigated, even though the resulting theory will not be so simple, fresh discoveries may be made, throwing a valuable light on the true forms of molecules.

This cannot tell us about the insides of molecules, but only how the molecules behave when they collide. Two molecules which collide sufficiently violently may be able to break each other up into atoms, but violent collisions like this hardly ever occur in an ordinary gas. In an ordinary collision, gas molecules do not come into intimate contact, but push each other away before more than their outworks have become involved. It is the properties of these outworks, or more precisely of the forces which they exert on each other, that can be found by constructing a theory which will fit the experiments more closely.

In this new theory, the molecules have still to be regarded as round, for the sake of simplicity. This is not really correct, but fortunately, because molecules push each other away before any "corners" on them can come into contact, any irregularities of shape exert very little influence on collisions. The chief difference from rigid elastic spheres is that the molecules are "soft"; that is, the force between them does not suddenly act, like the force when billiard-balls collide, but increases steadily as the molecules approach each other, like the force between two soft rubber balls hitting each other. The information which we seek is regarding the way in which the force between molecules varies with the distance.

We already know roughly how this force must vary. A liquid holds together, even though its molecules are moving rapidly to and fro; thus the molecules must attract each other when they try to move apart. Equally the liquid is nearly incompressible; thus the molecules must violently repel each other when they get too close together. There is no certainty that molecules in a gas must behave in the same way as in a liquid; but if they do, the force between two molecules must be attractive at sufficiently great distances, but violently repulsive at small.

A striking proof that gas molecules, like liquid molecules, tend to cling together was supplied by some experiments by Joule and Thomson. If a gas expands in normal circumstances, it cools, because it has to do work in pushing back whatever encloses it; when it expands through a porous plug, however, it does not have to push anything back, and so should not cool. But Joule and Thomson found that when air seeped through a porous plug from a vessel where the pressure was high to one where it was low, it arrived on the low-pressure side cooler than when it started. The reason is that, even though the air does not have to do work in pushing anything back, it has to do work in expanding against forces that make the molecules cling together.

Other gases were found to behave like air; but hydrogen showed a very slight heating after expansion. This does mean that hydrogen molecules never cling together; hydrogen does liquefy, even though not until the temperature is very low. But in hydrogen the attractive forces are weak, and at ordinary temperatures the short-range repulsive forces between

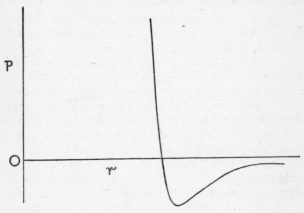

FIG. 7

Variation of the force P between two molecules as the distance between them varies, taking

$$P = \frac{K}{r^s} - \frac{L}{r^t},$$

with $s = 11$, $t = 7$

the molecules affect them more, even in expanding through a porous plug.

For the purposes of theory, the force P between two molecules whose centres are a distance r apart is often supposed to be given by an equation of the form

$$P = \frac{K}{r^s} - \frac{L}{r^t}, \qquad . \qquad . \qquad . \qquad (30)$$

where K, L, s, and t are positive, and s is greater than t (see

Fig. 7). If r is small, the term K/r^s in this is larger than L/r^t, and P is positive, representing a repulsion; if r is large, L/r^t is the larger term, and P is negative (attractive). Again, if r is large, K/r^s and L/r^t are both small; thus (30) correctly indicates that the attraction at large distances is much smaller than the repulsion at small. In fact, an equation like (30) seems to give not a bad representation of the force between molecules. Modern atomic theory has shown that the attraction between molecules can be represented fairly accurately by a term $-L/r^t$, with $t = 7$; the representation of the repulsion at small distances by the term K/r^s is, however, not quite as good.

Theoretically, the ideal course to pursue would be to assume an equation of the form (30), and to determine K, L, s, and t to make theory and experiment agree as closely as possible. In practice this turns out to be quite impracticable; four constants are far too many to determine at once. Even if, guided by atomic theory, t is taken as 7, several groups of different values of K, L, and s give almost equally good agreement with experiment. For this reason simpler force-laws are often assumed. Sometimes the attractive term $-L/r^t$ in (30) is altogether omitted, and the molecules are supposed to repel each other at all distances. Another possible assumption is that the molecules are rigid spheres surrounded by attractive fields of force; this can be got from (30) by taking the limit as $s \to \infty$ For, write (30) in the form

$$P = \frac{K}{a^s}\left(\frac{a}{r}\right)^s - \frac{L}{r^t}$$

and suppose that, as $s \to \infty$, K/a^s remains finite. Then, in the limit, the first term on the right becomes indefinitely small when r is greater than a, indefinitely large when r is less than a. That is, there is no repulsive force when r is greater than a, but an indefinitely great repulsion appears when $r = a$ and stops the molecules from approaching further.

Simpler laws of force like these involve fewer unknown constants than (30), and these constants can be determined uniquely from experiment. But this advantage over (30) is offset by the fact that such simpler laws do not represent the physical facts anything like as well as (30).

Deviations from Boyle's Law

An ideal gas obeying Boyle's and Charles's laws exactly is called a perfect gas. Perfection is a state never actually attained in practice, either by men or gases; but actual gases are nearly perfect at moderate pressures. At great pressures matters are different; the product pV of pressure and volume does not remain exactly constant, at a given temperature, as the pressure increases. Experiments at the necessary high pressures are none too easy; for example, Amagat worked

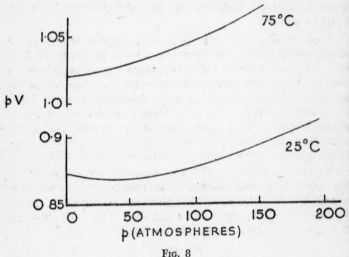

FIG. 8

Variation of pV with p for nitrogen at 25°C. and at 75°C.

in a mine-shaft, using the pressure of a column of mercury up to 300 metres long, with all the attendant inconveniences and dangers. Results obtained recently for nitrogen (by Michels and co-workers) are illustrated in Fig. 8. They show that, as a gas is compressed at a low temperature, pV first decreases slowly, and then increases much more rapidly; when it is compressed at higher temperatures, pV steadily increases.

These deviations from perfection were first explained by J. van der Waals in 1873, in terms of the finite size of the molecules and of their cohesion. Van der Waals supposed that the molecules could be represented with sufficient accuracy as rigid elastic spheres surrounded by attractive fields of force. This enabled him to treat the effects of finite size and of cohesion separately.

Consider first the effect of the finite size of the spheres; this increases the pressure by reducing the volume available to any one molecule. Let d be the diameter of a molecule; then d is also the distance between the centres of two colliding molecules at the instant of collision, and the centres of two molecules can never be less than a distance d apart. Suppose a sphere of radius d is drawn round the centre of each molecule; this sphere delimits a region from which the centres of all other molecules are debarred. Hence, if N molecules are present in a volume V, a given molecule's centre is barred from entering a volume equal to that of $N - 1$ of these spheres. Because N is in practice enormous, this volume is indistinguishable from the volume of N such spheres; the volume is denoted by $2b$, so that b is four times the volume of the molecules inside V, i.e.

$$b = \tfrac{2}{3}\pi d^3 N. \qquad . \qquad . \qquad . \quad (31)$$

Since the centre of each molecule is excluded from a part $2b$ of the total volume V, it is natural to expect that the Boyle-Charles equation, i.e.

$$pV = NkT$$

should be corrected by replacing V by $V - 2b$. But this is not so; V should be replaced by $V - b$, not $V - 2b$, and the corrected form of the equation is

$$p(V - b) = NkT. \qquad . \qquad . \qquad (32)$$

For, to ensure that the centre A of one molecule should not be closer than a distance d from the centre B of a second, it is sufficient to say *either* that A cannot lie within a sphere round B, *or* that B cannot lie within a sphere round A; it is not necessary to make both of these statements at the same time. In surrounding the centre of *each* molecule simultaneously by a sphere, and excluding the centre of each sphere from the volume of all other spheres, the excluded volumes are being counted twice. Hence, as equation (32) indicates, V should be decreased by b, not $2b$.

The pressure on the walls and that across an internal surface in the gas are both increased by the same amount by reason of the finite size of the molecules (they must be if the gas is to remain in equilibrium); but the mechanism of the increase is rather different in the two cases. The surface pressure is increased because the molecules have a decreased effective volume $V - b$ in which to move, and so hit the surface more often. The pressure across an internal surface is increased by what occurs at collisions. The mere act of collision between molecules with centres A and B transfers momentum from A to B. Thus collisions such that A and B are on opposite sides of the internal surface result in a transfer of momentum across the surface, additional to the transfer by molecules crossing the surface. This collisional transfer of momentum gives rise to the increase in the internal pressure.

A further correction for the finite size of molecules should also strictly be made to allow for the fact that the centres of molecules cannot approach closer than $\frac{1}{2}d$ to the walls of the containing vessel. But since such a correction would reduce the size of the vessel only by one or two hundred-millionths of a centimetre, it would in practice be completely negligible.

Van der Waals' second correction refers to the inter-molecular attractions. These also affect the internal and boundary pressures differently. In the middle of the gas, a molecule is being pulled in all directions by the attractions of other molecules round it, and the resultant effect of these attractions is, on an average, nil. Near the boundary, however, a molecule is subject to attractions from other molecules on one side of it only. Thus as it approaches the boundary it is slowed down by the backward pull of the others; it strikes the boundary so much the less violently, and the boundary pressure is thereby reduced.

If the internal pressure were still regarded simply as the rate of transfer of momentum per unit area across an internal surface, it would be greater than the boundary pressure. In order to count the internal pressure as still equal to the boundary pressure, we must include in it the total force across the internal surface, exerted by molecules on one side on molecules on the other.

This force is a traction, or negative pressure, similar, save as regards sign, to the pressure which Newton supposed a gas to exert because of the mutual repulsions of the molecules; but it is supposed to be contributed only by molecules very near the internal surface, and so not to depend, like Newton's pressure, on the shape of the containing vessel. It is proportional to the number of attracting molecules, and to the number of attracted molecules; since each of these numbers is proportional to the density, i.e. for a given mass of gas, inversely proportional to V, the traction is a/V^2, where a is a constant. Hence, to correct for attractive forces, the pressure given by (32) must be reduced by a/V^2; that is, (32) must be replaced by

$$(p + a/V^2)(V - b) = NkT \qquad . \qquad . \qquad (33)$$

which is van der Waals's gas equation.

In equation (33), a and b are constant for a given mass of gas; if, however, the total amount of the gas considered be varied, b varies like N, and a like N^2.

Van der Waals's Equation

Equation (33) represents the behaviour of actual gases a good deal more closely than does the Boyle-Charles equation $pV = NkT$. In a moderately rare gas, for which a and b are small, it is hardly distinguishable from the Boyle-Charles equation. To see the behaviour which it predicts in gases under fairly great pressures, the equation is written in the form

$$\left(\frac{p}{p_o} + \frac{V_o^2}{V^2}\right)\left(\frac{V}{V_o} - 1\right) = \frac{T}{T_o}$$

where $V_o = b$, $p_o = a/b^2$, $T_o = a/(Nkb)$. This equation is the same for all gases, save that V_o, p_o and T_o differ from gas to gas. For a special value of T/T_o, the equation relates p/p_o with V/V_o, and so a curve can be drawn, showing how pV/p_oV_o varies as p/p_o increases. Curves like this are drawn for several different values of T/T_o in Fig. 9. Precisely the same set of curves are found for all gases. If curves are drawn for two distinct gases, showing how pV varies as p increases for different temperatures, to each curve for the first gas corresponds a curve for the second, such that T/T_o has the same value for the two curves, and p/p_o and V/V_o are the same at corresponding points of the two. In other words, the set of curves for the one gas can be used for the other, if the horizontal and vertical scales are altered, and also the temperature-scale by which the curves are distinguished.

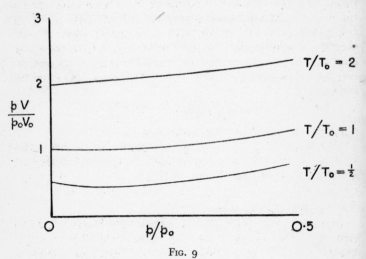

Fig. 9

Variation of pV with p at different temperatures, according to van der Waals' law.

This is the law of corresponding states, a law which experiment shows to be reasonably well obeyed by many gases.

Fig. 9 shows that, if the temperature is less than T_o, pV first decreases as p increases, and then increases; if the temperature exceeds T_o, on the other hand, pV steadily increases as p increases. If the temperature is actually equal to T_o, pV is nearly constant near $p = 0$, so that Boyle's law is very nearly obeyed. Roughly speaking, the effect of the attractions of the molecules dominates that of their finite size if the gas is not too much compressed, and the molecules are moving sufficiently slowly to give the attractions enough time to take effect before one molecule passes another.

Behaviour like this is observed for actual gases; pV always increases if p becomes large enough, but it decreases with increasing pressure for small pressures if the temperature is small enough. The temperature T_0, below which the molecules' attractions are dominant at low pressures, is about 60°C. for nitrogen, but less than -160°C. for hydrogen, whose molecules attract each other only weakly.

However, though van der Waals' equation predicts many features of the actual behaviour of gases, it does not really apply to very dense gases. It makes p infinite if the volume of the gas is b, i.e. four times the volume of the molecules; but the pressure ought not to be infinite until the molecules are packed as tightly as they can be, and if so packed they would fill a volume much less than four times their own volume.

This difficulty arises because in the proof of van der Waals' equation any one molecule was supposed to be excluded from $N-1$ spheres of radius d round the other molecules; but these spheres may overlap, and so the excluded volume is over-estimated. At fairly low pressures the overlapping can be ignored, but not at high. Again, the traction due to forces between the molecules is proportional to $1/V^2$ only if it is not too strong. If attractions between the molecules are very strong, they may draw gas away from the walls of the vessel, so that, near the walls, the density is less than in the middle of the gas; they may also collect the molecules together into groups. Finally, the attractive forces may make molecules collide which would not otherwise have done so, and so increase the collisional transfer of momentum across an internal surface. For all these reasons, van der Waals's law is only an approximation, valid only at moderate densities.

Molecular Constants

The important question, however, is not how well—or, to be more exact, how badly—van der Waals's law applies to very dense gases, but what can be learnt from it about molecular fields when it does apply. The equation

$$\left(p + \frac{a}{V^2}\right)(V - b) = NkT$$

applies strictly only if the cohesive part a/V^2 is small compared with the total pressure p, and the excluded volume b is small compared with the total volume V. This means that the product of the two small terms a/V^2 and b on the left-hand side of the equation can be neglected, so that the equation can be written

$$pV = NkT + pb - a/V.$$

Again, in the small term a/V, the slight deviation from Boyle's law $pV = NkT$ can be neglected, and so

$$pV = NkT + pb - ap/NkT,$$

$$= NkT + p\left(b - \frac{a}{NkT}\right) \qquad . \qquad . \qquad (34)$$

This equation, like van der Waals's original equation, is valid only when the gas is not too compressed.

According to (34), if pV is plotted against p for a given temperature (as in Fig. 8), the resulting curve at any temperature should be a straight line whose slope is $b - a/NkT$. That is, since (34) is valid only when p is small, the slope of curves like those of Fig. 7 when p is small gives $b - a/NkT$. Now NkT is known (it is the value of pV for very small pressures); hence if $b - a/NkT$ is known for two temperatures, a and b can be found. Thus, for example, for air at N.T.P. the values of a and b are found to be such that the cohesive term a/V^2 reduces the total pressure by about 0·26 per cent, and that b is about 0·21 per cent of the whole volume occupied by the gas. Similar results are obtained for most other gases.

The value of b can be used, together with the experimental value of the viscosity, to estimate the number n of molecules per cubic centimetre of the gas. From the viscosity, the mean free path of a molecule can be estimated; it is given by

$$l = \frac{1}{\sqrt{2\pi nd^2}}$$

Also b is given by

$$b = \tfrac{2}{3}\pi d^3 N = \tfrac{2}{3}\pi d^3 nV.$$

Thus

$$bl = \frac{\sqrt{2}}{3}Vd$$

giving d; and when its value is substituted into one of the other equations, n can be found.

An estimate of n by such means is, however, bound to be rather inaccurate, since the viscosity formula in any case does not take account of cohesive forces. Since n is known more accurately by other methods, it is better to use b for an independent determination of the size of a molecule. Thus, for example, the radius of a hydrogen molecule, as estimated from the value of b, is $1 \cdot 27 \times 10^{-8}$ cm., while the value got from viscosity measures is about $1 \cdot 36 \times 10^{-8}$ cm. In view of the fact that the first estimate takes cohesive forces into account, and the second does not, the agreement between the two is not bad.

Van der Waals's other constant a measures the total cohesion produced by the mutual attractions of molecules. This total cohesion may be due to forces which are strong for molecules nearly in contact, but fall off rapidly as the molecules separate, or to forces which are weaker at short distances, but extend further. The theory of van der Waals's equation cannot by itself tell us which of these is true; but, as mentioned above, atomic theory shows that the forces vary roughly as the inverse seventh power of the distance.

Suppose that the attraction between two molecules is L/r^t when their centres are a distance r apart. Then a general method, known as the method of dimensions, can be used to prove that

$$a = CN^2L/d^{t-4}$$

where C is a pure number. The argument is as follows. The traction (negative pressure) a/V^2 is a force per unit area; since the volume V is given by the cube of some length, a is given by a force times the fourth power of a length. We already know that a is proportional to N^2; since N is simply a pure number, a/N^2 is also given by a force times the fourth power of a length. But the only forces on which a/N^2 can depend are the forces between molecules, which at any distance are always multiples of the force L/d^t between molecules in contact; the only lengths on which it can depend are multiples of d, the diameter of a molecule. Hence a/N^2 must be a multiple of $L/d^t \times d^4$, i.e. of L/d^{t-4}.

An exact calculation shows that, when the attraction between two molecules is L/r^7,

$$a = \frac{\pi N^2 L}{9d^3}$$

This enables us to fix L, given a. For example, for nitrogen at N.T.P., the force between two molecules is found to be such that work equal to about four-fifths of the mean kinetic energy of a molecule would be needed to separate two molecules which are in contact. This indicates a fairly strong

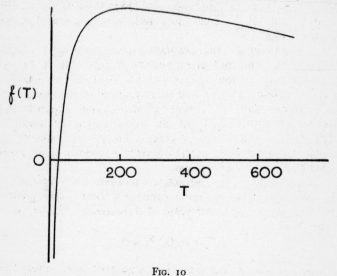

FIG. 10

Variation of $f(T)$ with the absolute temperature T for helium.

attraction, and one which makes the neglect of attractions in viscosity work appear rather dubious. Gases like carbon dioxide, which are more easily liquefied, show even stronger attractions; hydrogen and helium, which are only liquefied at very low temperatures, show much weaker attractions, as is to be expected.

Repulsive Forces

This, however, does not exhaust the information to be derived from gas pressures. Equation (34), which has just been used to determine the constants a and b, can be put in the form

$$pV = NkT + pf(T) \qquad \cdot \qquad \cdot \qquad (35)$$

where

$$f(T) = b - \frac{a}{NkT}$$

The value of $f(T)$ for any T can be got from the experimental results by plotting pV against p, and taking the slope of the corresponding curve when p is small. When T is small, cohesive forces (represented by the constant a) determine the sign of $f(T)$; when T is large, this sign is determined by the finite size of the molecules (represented by b). For very great values of T, $f(T)$ should tend to the constant limiting value b.

Fig. 10 shows the experimental values of $f(T)$, obtained by plotting pV against p for helium. Cohesive forces are small for this gas, and so $f(T)$ is negative only when the temperature is less than about 25° absolute, or − 248°C. The remarkable feature is, however, the behaviour of $f(T)$ at large temperatures. Instead of tending to a constant limiting value, $f(T)$ begins to decrease when T is about − 100°C. It is as if b were not constant, but decreased slowly as T increased; that is, since b is four times the volume of the molecules, as if the size of a molecule decreases with increasing temperature.

Now this is just what is to be expected from the softness of actual molecules. Ignore cohesion for the moment; then the force between molecules can be taken as a repulsion falling off with increasing distance. If the temperature increases, the molecules move faster, and remain in each other's repulsive fields for a shorter time. Thus they disturb each other's paths less when they meet; the effect is the same as if they were spheres of smaller radius (see Fig. 11).

To see how the effective diameter d varies with the temperature, suppose the repulsion between two molecules is K/r^s when their centres are a distance r apart. Then the method of dimensions indicates that

$$d = C' \left(\frac{K}{kT} \right)^{\frac{1}{s-1}} \qquad \cdot \qquad \cdot \qquad (36)$$

where C' is a pure number, depending on s. For $\frac{3}{2} kT$ is the mean kinetic energy of a molecule, and energy is measured by force times distance. But the only distance which can appear in our calculations is d, or some multiple of it; the only force is the force between two molecules when at such a distance apart. Hence $\frac{3}{2} kT$ is a multiple of $d \times K/d^s$; whence the result. Otherwise stated, the result is that d is a distance comparable with the separation at which the potential energy of repulsion of two molecules equals the kinetic energy $\frac{3}{2} kT$ (it is actually just a little greater than this separation).

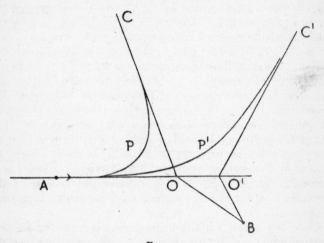

FIG. 11

Motion of a molecule A relative to a molecule B, under their mutual repulsion. When A moves slowly relative to B, it travels along the path APC; its deflection is the same as if it travelled along AO, and at O suffered a violent collision making it to move along OC; OB would be the sum of the radii of the molecules for such a collision to occur. When A moves more rapidly, its path becomes $AP'C'$; the sum of the radii in an equivalent collision is now the smaller distance $O'B$.

According to (36), the apparent volume of the molecules should vary like $T^{3/(s-1)}$, and so, from the behaviour of $f(T)$ at large temperatures, s can be found. For example, the experimental results for helium can be fitted very well by taking $s = 13$. The calculation of s for other molecules is less certain, since the attractive forces between the molecules are much larger for most other gases, and are not negligible, even at fairly high temperatures. The probable value of s for most other gases is, however, a little lower than for helium—in the neighbourhood of 10 or 11.

Viscosity and Molecular Fields

The force between two molecules can also be determined from the dependence of the viscosity μ on the temperature. The viscosity is given by

$$\mu = 0.499 \, \rho l \bar{c},$$

where l is the mean free path, and $\bar{c}$ the mean molecular speed. In this, $\bar{c}$ is proportional to the square root of the temperature T, and l is given by

$$l = \frac{1}{\sqrt{2\pi n d^2}}.$$

Thus if the diameter d of a molecule does not depend on the temperature, we should find that for actual gases

$$\mu \propto T^{\frac{1}{2}}.$$

Actually, experiments show that μ varies more rapidly than $T^{\frac{1}{2}}$. Maxwell thought that some experiments which he made showed that $\mu \propto T$; but the true law of variation is rather slower than this for most gases, lying between $\mu \propto T^{\frac{3}{4}}$ and $\mu \propto T$.

This can be explained in terms of the softness of the molecules. If molecules actually repel each other with a force K/r^s, then, as (36) indicates, their effective diameter is proportional to $T^{-1/(s-1)}$. Hence the viscosity is proportional to $d^{-2}T^{\frac{1}{2}}$, i.e. to T^q, where

$$q = \tfrac{1}{2} + \frac{2}{s-1}. \qquad \cdot \qquad \cdot \qquad \cdot \qquad (37)$$

For hydrogen and helium, μ is roughly proportional to $T^{\frac{3}{4}}$, showing that s is about 13, as found in last section. Other gases do not give a law $\mu \propto T^q$ exactly, but, if the value of q is chosen to give the closest possible agreement with a law $\mu \propto T^q$, the results do not agree at all closely with those got by studying the deviations from Boyle's law. Oxygen and nitrogen give values of q between 8 and 9, and gases like carbon dioxide make q not much bigger than 5. This is impossibly low, since the attraction between two molecules varies like r^{-7}, and the repulsive part of the force between them must vary faster than this. Clearly the reason is that the attraction between the molecules is being neglected; this is not very strong for hydrogen and helium, but stronger for other gases.

Attractions between molecules affect the viscosity and the pressure in very different ways. Repulsions between molecules increase the pressure, attractions decrease it; but attractions

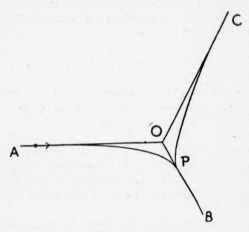

FIG. 12

Motion of the centre A of one attracting-sphere molecule relative to the centre B of another. The path described by A is APC, a collision of the molecules occurring at P. The deflection is the same as if A moved along straight lines AO, OC, a collision occurring at O; thus the attraction between the molecules effectively increases the sum of the radii from BP to BO.

and repulsions often co-operate to reduce the viscosity. The more readily molecules can carry momentum from point to point, the greater is the viscosity; and attractive forces can deflect molecules, and so check the transport of momentum, just as well as repulsive forces.

For example, suppose the molecules are represented by spheres weakly attracting each other. Molecules which pass each other are hardly affected by the attractions unless they get fairly close to each other. But if they do get fairly close together, they are likely to be deflected so that they hit each other. That is, the attractions make molecules collide which would otherwise not have done so; effectively, they increase the size of the molecules (see Fig. 12). As the temperature increases, however, this apparent increase in the size becomes less; molecules are moving faster, and so the attractions have less time to deflect them and make them collide. At very great temperatures, the apparent increase in size would disappear.

The actual law of increase in size can again be found by the method of dimensions. Suppose the force between two molecules to be L/r^t at a distance r. The free path depends on the square of the diameter d; suppose that attractions increase the effective value of this to D^2, where

$$D^2 = d^2 (1 + l).$$

In this equation, l is a pure number, proportional to the attractive forces whose effect it represents, and depending on the speeds of the molecules, i.e. on their mean kinetic energy $\frac{3}{2}kT$. Now the only other energy or work with which we can compare $\frac{3}{2}kT$ is the work done by the attractive force between molecules $- L/d^t$, or some fraction of it—in moving a distance which is some number of times d. Thus the only pure number which we can construct out of the ingredients to hand is the ratio of the two energies

$$L/d^{t-1} : \frac{3}{2}kT$$

or some function of it; and since l is proportional to attractive forces, i.e. to L, the equation for l must be of the form

$$l = \frac{C'' L}{d^{t-1} kT}$$

where C'' is a numerical constant. If $t = 7$, C'' is about 0·03.

It is customary to put

$$l = \frac{S}{T}, \quad D^2 = d^2 \left(1 + \frac{S}{T}\right).$$

In this, S is called Sutherland's constant. Since the viscosity μ is proportional to $T^{\frac{1}{2}} D^{-2}$, this gives

$$\mu \propto T^{\frac{1}{2}} / \left(1 + \frac{S}{T} \right) \qquad . \qquad . \qquad . \qquad (38)$$

in place of $\mu \propto T^{\frac{1}{2}}$. This formula gives very nearly the actual variation of viscosity with temperature for several gases, notably oxygen and nitrogen; but none the less it cannot be regarded as satisfactory from the theoretical standpoint. For example, the value of S for nitrogen is about 110; this implies attractions between the molecules so strong that the potential energy of two molecules in contact would be about one and a half times the mean kinetic energy of a molecule. This is far bigger than was found from van der Waals's law; it is, moreover, so big that the molecules cannot be regarded as weakly attracting, and (38) is strictly valid only when they do attract weakly.

Unsatisfactory conclusions were, in any case, more or less inevitable, even apart from this. The actual law of variation of μ with temperature depends both on the attractions of the molecules and on the softness of their repulsive fields, and neglect of either of these cannot fail to lead to trouble. But though it is easy to see what is wrong, it is less easy to right it. If the attractions are at all strong, they not only cause molecules to collide which otherwise would not have done so; they also deflect molecules considerably on their own account.

When allowance is made for this, a simple mathematical treatment of the viscosity becomes almost impossible. Thus, up to the present, viscosity data have not, save in a few cases, yielded the harvest of information about molecular fields which might be hoped. This is especially unfortunate, for they seem very suitable for use in determining the repulsive part of the field. However, the story is not finished yet, and it may still have a happier ending.

Unlike Molecules

Experimental results on diffusion and on thermal diffusion can also give information about the forces between molecules.

For example, the coefficient of self-diffusion D_{11} is connected with the viscosity μ by the equation

$$D_{11} = j\mu/\rho.$$

For rigid spherical molecules, j is 1·2; for other molecular models, theory gives rather higher values of j. By determining the experimental value of j in those few cases in which D_{11} can be found, a little can be found about the force between the molecules. Thus for hydrogen, for example, the experimental value of j is 1·36; this can be explained by supposing the molecules to repel each other with a force varying roughly as the twelfth power of the distance, which is consistent with results got from viscosity and from the deviations from Boyle's law. The amount of information which can be got in this way is, however, strictly limited, because the experimental results are few and not always easy to interpret.

The self-diffusion results refer to the forces between like molecules. The chief use of diffusion and thermal diffusion results is, however, to determine the forces between unlike molecules. These can also be determined by methods like those used earlier for like molecules. For example, by studying the p, V relation for a mixture of gases, the total effects of repulsive and attractive fields could be found; the parts due to like molecules could be determined from experiments with the pure gases which form the mixture, and the rest would give the forces between unlike molecules. In the same way, viscosity in a gas-mixture depends partly on collisions between like molecules, partly on collisions between unlike. But in practice neither of these methods has been used; experiments on diffusion, and especially on thermal diffusion, have proved easier to interpret.

The diffusion results are scanty, and not very reliable. The diffusion coefficient D_{12} of rigid spherical molecules is proportional to molecular speeds, and inversely proportional to the density; thus at a constant *pressure*, D_{12} is proportional to $T^{\frac{3}{2}}$ for rigid spherical molecules. For actual gases, D_{12} varies more rapidly than $T^{\frac{3}{2}}$; this is due to the softness of actual molecules, and to their mutual attraction. However, the scantiness of experimental results about diffusion makes it impossible to decide the relative importance of these two factors.

The most powerful method of studying forces between unlike molecules is undoubtedly that resting on thermal diffusion. As was noted in last chapter, thermal diffusion arises because fast molecules are handicapped as they try to move about from point to point; their extra speed simply makes them run into others more quickly. The degree of their handicap, however, depends on what happens when they do run into others. Consider, for example, molecules repelling each other with a force K/r^s; these behave as if they had a diameter inversely proportional to $T^{1/(s-1)}$, i.e., roughly, to the $2/(s-1)$ power of the speed. Thus the free path of molecules of different speeds is, roughly speaking, proportional to the $4/(s-1)$ power of the speed; this reduces the handicap of fast molecules appreciably. If $s = 5$, the handicap completely disappears; fast molecules do run into others more quickly than slow, but their speed means that they slip past the molecules which they meet without these having time to deflect them in their courses. Thus if $s = 5$ thermal diffusion disappears completely. This is why Maxwell was not able to isolate thermal diffusion, for his most accurate work assumed molecules repelling with a force K/r^5. If s is greater than 5, thermal diffusion does not completely disappear, but its strength is much less than it would be for rigid molecules. By comparing its actual strength with that to be expected if the molecules were elastic spheres, the value of s can be found.

The determination is none too easy in practice. Thermal diffusion is due, in the first place, to the fact that molecules are carrying heat from point to point, the faster of the molecules suffering from the handicap which has been mentioned. Since the extent to which molecules can carry heat is limited by every sort of collision between them, collisions between like molecules, as well as those between unlike, have to be taken into account in the theory of thermal diffusion. Values of s have, in fact, been calculated for several pairs of gases; they are rather lower than would be expected, ranging from 7 for mixtures of fairly soft molecules like those of nitrogen and argon, to 11·5 for mixtures of hard molecules like helium and neon.

A force varying like K/r^s is, of course, not exactly true to nature, which demands a force which is attractive at large distances; if account were taken of cohesive forces, the repulsive part of the force between molecules would almost certainly be found to vary inversely as a much greater power of the distance. Mathematical difficulties have, however, thus far prevented a discussion of more natural laws of force.

To sum up this chapter, gas-theory enables us to determine some of the properties of molecular exteriors. It does not give a complete picture of those properties, and the properties which it can determine have not all been fully worked out as yet. But it has given a fairly clear picture of the externals of molecules, and this picture has been most useful in other branches of science.

CHAPTER VIII

THE INSIDES OF GAS MOLECULES

Internal Energy

SINCE Chapter III, the historical aspect of gas-theory has rather tended to disappear from view. This was natural; by about 1860 the foundations of the subject had been well and truly laid, and the quest for a sound base of a theory was replaced by the building of a solid structure on the foundation—a more prosaic procedure. The building of that structure has been the subject of the last few chapters. But now it is time to return to the history of fundamentals, at the point at which this was left.

Most of the normal behaviour of gases depends only on the outworks of the molecules, and tells us nothing about their make-up. The heat of the gas is, however, in part contributed by internal energy, and so a study of its heat tells a little about the inside of a molecule. As soon as the heat was studied in detail, difficulties arose, and these became continually more clamant until at last a whole new theory of the interior of molecules had to be invented. It would be wholly wrong to pretend that this new theory was invented wholly, or even mainly, to clear up difficulties about the energy of gases; but such difficulties provided one of the more important reasons for the new theory.

As was seen in Chapter III, Clausius suggested that the heat of a gas is greater than the ordinary (translatory) kinetic energy of the molecules simply because the molecules have internal energy as well as energy of translation. The internal energy has many forms; energy of rotation and energy of internal vibration are two of them. To discuss either of these, we must make use of a simple model of a molecule.

In considering rotation, it is simplest to think of molecules as spheres spinning about a diameter. The rate of rotation is fixed by the angular velocity ω, the angle (in radians) turned per second. This is treated as a vector quantity, its direction being taken as the direction of the diameter about which the sphere turns. Call the vector $\boldsymbol{\omega}$; it can be represented by a line OP drawn parallel to the diameter, whose length is proportional to the rate of rotation (Fig. 13). If Ox, Oy and Oz are three mutually perpendicular lines, the displacement OP can be divided into three parts OM, MN and NP parallel to these lines; these give the components ω_x, ω_y and ω_z of $\boldsymbol{\omega}$ parallel to Ox, Oy and Oz. These components are genuinely parts into which $\boldsymbol{\omega}$ can, in an appropriate sense, be divided. If the sphere turns about the diameter parallel to Ox at a rate ω_x, let the velocity of some point Q of it be $\boldsymbol{V}_x$; and let $\boldsymbol{V}_y$, $\boldsymbol{V}_z$ similarly be the velocities of Q when the sphere turns about diameters parallel to Oy or Oz at rates ω_y or ω_z. Then $\boldsymbol{V}$, the velocity of Q when the sphere turns with the angular velocity $\boldsymbol{\omega}$, is the sum of $\boldsymbol{V}_x$, $\boldsymbol{V}_y$ and $\boldsymbol{V}_z$, these being added by the rule for adding vector displacements (see Fig. 13).

The kinetic energy of the sphere due to its rotation $\boldsymbol{\omega}$ is also the sum of the kinetic energies of the rotations ω_x, ω_y and ω_z taken separately. The kinetic energy is $\frac{1}{2}I\omega^2$, where I is a quantity whose exact nature need not be specified, called the moment of inertia of the molecule. The kinetic energies of the separate rotations ω_x, ω_y and ω_z are similarly $\frac{1}{2}I\omega_x^2$, etc.; thus

$$\tfrac{1}{2}I\omega^2 = \tfrac{1}{2}I\omega_x^2 + \tfrac{1}{2}I\omega_y^2 + \tfrac{1}{2}I\omega_z^2.$$

This is very like the equation

$$\tfrac{1}{2}mc^2 = \tfrac{1}{2}mu^2 + \tfrac{1}{2}mv^2 + \tfrac{1}{2}mw^2$$

expressing the total kinetic energy of translation of a molecule
moving with velocity **c** as the sum of the kinetic energies due
to the components of **c**. The formulae differ only by replacing

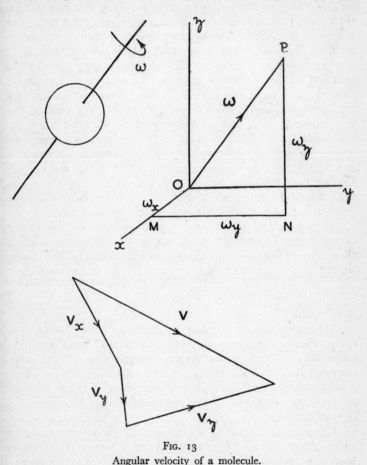

FIG. 13
Angular velocity of a molecule.

the linear velocity **c** by the angular velocity **ω** and the mass m
by the moment of inertia I.

To consider internal vibrations, an altogether different
model of a molecule is needed. In this case we can suppose

the molecule to consist of two equal atoms, which can be pictured as small solid spheres connected by a rubber rod, the whole looking rather like a dumb-bell. A vibration consists of the atoms moving to and fro along the line joining them, the rubber rod first contracting, then expanding. The molecule as a whole can have a velocity in any direction; in addition the two atoms have at any instant equal speeds C, say, in opposite directions. The kinetic energy due to the speeds C is $\frac{1}{2}mC^2$, where m is the total mass of the molecule. As the atoms separate, their kinetic energy is converted into potential energy of the rod (strain energy) until at last they come to rest, and all the energy is potential; then the rod pulls them together again, and the potential energy is converted back into kinetic; the rod next becomes compressed, and the energy becomes potential once more; and so on. During the vibration, roughly speaking, the energy is potential for half the time, and kinetic for the other half; the mean potential energy equals the mean kinetic energy.

Of course, real molecules are nothing like rotating spheres or vibrating dumbbells; they are much more complicated than these. But by considering simple models like these, insight can be gained into the properties of real molecules.

Equipartition

Molecules are set rotating or vibrating by collisions with each other. The rotations and vibrations complicate the collisions greatly; but the average energies due to their existence can be calculated, using an argument like that by which it was proved in Chapter II that molecules of different gases at the same temperature have the same average kinetic energy of translation.

Consider first rotating molecules, which we are regarding as spinning spheres. The argument of Chapter II began by asserting that one set of velocities which gives the correct total energy is just as likely as any other. Similarly, we here assert that any one set of velocities and angular velocities jointly giving the correct total energy is just as likely as any other. The assertion, like that of Chapter II, is one which can be justified by a detailed proof. Though the proof will not be attempted here, the assertion appears at least to be a reasonable generalization of the earlier one.

The total energy of the molecules is made up of the energy of their motions from point to point ($\frac{1}{2}mc^2$) and the energy of their rotations ($\frac{1}{2}I\omega^2$). To see how these are related, compare the gas being considered, one with N molecules, say, with a second gas composed of $2N$ non-rotating molecules, all with the same mass m. The velocities of N of the molecules of the second gas are supposed to be the velocities $\mathbf{c}$ of the molecules of the first gas; the velocities $\mathbf{c}'$ of the remaining N molecules of the second gas are supposed to be connected with the angular velocities ω of the molecules of the first by the equation

$$\mathbf{c}' = \sqrt{(I/m)}\ \boldsymbol{\omega}.$$

This means that the kinetic energy $\frac{1}{2}m c'^2$ of one of these last molecules is the kinetic energy of rotation, $\frac{1}{2}I\omega^2$, of one of the original molecules, and the total energy of the new gas equals that of the old. Since one set of velocities $\mathbf{c}$ and angular velocities ω of the original gas is just as probable as any other giving the same total energy, one set of velocities $\mathbf{c}$ and $\mathbf{c}'$ of the molecules of the second gas is also just as probable as any other giving the same total energy. That is, the second gas has just the same properties as any other gas of $2N$ molecules; in particular, the second N of its molecules has just the same average energy as the first. Hence the molecules of the first gas have an average energy of rotation equal to their average energy of translation, i.e. $\frac{3}{2}kT$ per molecule.

The same type of argument can be applied to internal vibrations. Consider the "vibrating dumb-bell" molecule, discussed earlier. Any set of internal and external velocities of the molecules is now to be taken to be just as probable as any other giving the same total energy. The internal motion of a molecule as it vibrates takes place along a straight line, and so is best compared with another motion in a special direction, say with the part of the motion of the same molecule which is parallel to Ox. It is just as probable that, at a given instant, the kinetic energies of vibration and of motion parallel to Ox should be E_1 and E_2 as that they should be E_2 and E_1. Thus the average vibrational kinetic energy of the molecule equals the average kinetic energy of motion parallel to Ox, i.e. $\frac{1}{2}kT$. This does not give all the energy of vibration; during a vibration kinetic energy is continually being converted into potential energy, and then converted back, and the average potential energy equals the average kinetic energy. The total energy of vibration is the sum of kinetic and potential energies, kT per molecule.

These results can be stated in a different form. A molecule possesses three "degrees of freedom" in translatory motion; it can move in three independent directions, parallel to Ox, Oy and Oz (say, forward, sideways, or upward), and its most general motion is a combination of the three. The mean energy corresponding to one of these degrees of freedom—say that of motion parallel to Ox—is $\frac{1}{2}kT$, and the total energy of translation, $\frac{3}{2}kT$ per molecule, is the sum of parts corresponding to the three degrees of freedom. Similarly a rotating sphere has three degrees of freedom to turn; it can spin about diameters parallel to Ox, Oy or Oz, and its most general spin is a combination of the three. The mean energy $\frac{3}{2}kT$ of rotating molecules is again the sum of parts $\frac{1}{2}kT$ corresponding to each of the degrees of freedom. Again, a vibrating dumb-bell has two degrees of freedom to possess energy of vibration; it can vibrate only along one line, but it can possess both kinetic and potential energies. Once more, each degree of freedom contributes $\frac{1}{2}kT$ to the total energy.

This enables us to generalize our results to apply to less artificial and more general models of molecules than have yet been considered. If a molecule has s degrees of freedom to possess energy, due to its translation, its rotation, and its internal vibrations, its energy must be $s \times \frac{1}{2}kT$. For example, a dumb-bell molecule might be supposed to rotate, but not to rotate about its axis of symmetry (the line joining the centres of its two atoms); if so, it loses one rotational degree of freedom, and its average rotational energy becomes kT, not $\frac{3}{2}kT$.

Again, a molecule with three atoms can possess three distinct internal vibrations. For example, if the three atoms are in a line, and the two wing atoms are equal, the three vibrations shown in Fig. 14 could occur; in one the centre atom is at rest, and the wing ones vibrate in opposite senses; in the others the two wing atoms move in one direction and the centre one in the opposite direction, either along or perpendicular to the line joining them. The three vibrations take place in different lengths of time; the most general vibratory motion is a complicated combination of the three. In this case the average vibratory energy should be $6 \times \frac{1}{2}kT$.

The general result is, then, that a molecule possesses the same mean energy $\frac{1}{2}kT$ corresponding to each of its degrees of freedom to possess energy of translation, rotation, or vibration. This is the general Principle of Equipartition of Energy.

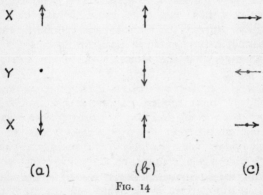

$$(a) \qquad (b) \qquad (c)$$

Fig. 14

The three oscillations (a), (b) and (c) of a triatomic linear molecule XYX. The dots show the rest positions of the atoms; in an oscillation, the atoms all move first towards the head of an arrow, and then towards its tail.

The Gathering Clouds

The equipartition principle is very beautiful in theory, but in practice it caused many headaches. By equation (12), given in the end of Chapter III, it implies that γ, the ratio of the specific heats of a gas, is given by

$$\gamma = 1 + \frac{2}{s}$$

where s is the number of degrees of freedom of the gas to possess energy. Thus the number of degrees of freedom can be calculated from an experimental value of γ, by the equation

$$s = \frac{2}{\gamma - 1}.$$

Maxwell made this calculation for air in 1875, soon after the discovery of the equipartition principle. He found $s = 4·9$, and commented that it was hard to interpret a molecule having such a number of degrees of freedom. In those days, however, it was easy to believe that the fault lay in some inadequacy of the theory. For example, if a molecule rotates so fast that it begins to stretch, its moment of inertia I is no longer a constant, and the analogy between the rotational energy $\frac{1}{2}I\omega^2$ and the translational energy $\frac{1}{2}mc^2$, on which was based the argument for equipartition, is no longer exact. If molecules spin so fast as to strain themselves, therefore, equipartition can only be approximate. Similarly, vibrational energy cannot exactly share in equipartition if the vibrations are so vigorous that the molecule begins to approach the breaking point.

This might explain $s = 4·9$ as a rough approximation to $s = 5$; indeed, more modern experiments have given values of s closer to 5 for air, and also for many diatomic gases. But how is one to interpret $s = 6·5$ (ammonia gas) or $s = 6·7$ (carbon dioxide)? Very few polyatomic gases give values of s anywhere near a whole number; some other sort of energy, not obeying the equipartition law, seems to be present.

The situation grows worse when one attempts to interpret the values of s derived for different gases. The monatomic gases—helium, neon, argon, etc.—give $s = 3$; this means that the molecules of such gases can only have translational energy, and cannot rotate. But why should they not rotate? They might be perfectly smooth; we do not meet perfectly smooth bodies in everyday life, but that is no reason why we should not meet them on going down to the molecular level; energy is always being wasted by friction in everyday life, but the energy of molecules does not waste. But even if molecules were smooth, they would be set rotating on collision if there were any knobs or protuberances on them which could strike against others. Only if they were featureless as well as smooth could they keep themselves from rotating.

Matters are very similar for the diatomic gases for which s is nearly 5. Using a "dumb-bell" picture for their molecules, the energy of such gases can be explained by supposing that they have only two degrees of freedom to rotate; they can turn about any line perpendicular to the dumb-bell axis, but not about the axis itself. This means again that the atoms must be smooth and featureless, or collisions would set them turning about the axis. On the other hand, any atom will, if appropriately stimulated, send out light of a definite wavelength characteristic of the atom; this indicates that it must have a definite structure to control the light sent out, and not be merely featureless. Why, then, should molecules not rotate in any way they please? And why should a dumb-bell molecule not vibrate?

The difficulties grew even worse when light-waves were taken into account. A light-wave was taken to be a vibration in the ether, a mysterious all-pervasive fluid much in vogue fifty years ago; the light-wave was set going by vibrations in atoms, and could set other atoms vibrating. Hence firstly, atoms must have internal energy corresponding to many vibrations; but with $s = 3$ or $s = 5$ or so, there was no room for such large energies. Also, secondly, the law of equipartition might be expected to apply to vibrations in the ether; the mean energy of each possible vibration ought to consist of $\frac{1}{2}kT$ of potential and $\frac{1}{2}kT$ of kinetic energy.

But the ether can vibrate with any frequency imaginable; it has therefore an infinite number of degrees of freedom to vibrate, and if energy is to be shared among all the available degrees of freedom the infinite number of degrees of freedom of the ether must take all, and leave none for the finite number of degrees of freedom of a molecule. In a rationing scheme where all individuals are treated alike, the largest families get the largest block ration; and the ether has so many mouths to be filled that there is nothing left for anything else.

Difficulties like these led Lord Kelvin, at the end of the nineteenth century, to speak of clouds obscuring the beauty and clearness of the theory which asserts that heat is a mode of motion. But the situation is worse than even he saw it. The specific heat of a gas is not constant; it normally increases with increasing temperature. For example, at ordinary temperatures the specific heat of hydrogen corresponds to $s = 5$ roughly; but as the temperature decreases the specific heat drops, and below $- 200°C.$ it corresponds roughly to $s = 3$

(see Fig. 15). That is, hydrogen seems to stop rotating at low temperatures.

Again, carbon dioxide has a specific heat corresponding to $s = 6 \cdot 7$ at $0°C.$; but at $600°C.$ its specific heat corresponds to s being greater than 10. It is as if its molecules have rotational energy at all temperatures, and vibrational energy at high temperatures, but they stop vibrating at low. Why should this happen? Of course, molecules should spin and vibrate less fast at low temperatures than at high, but the equipartition principle takes account of this. Here the problem

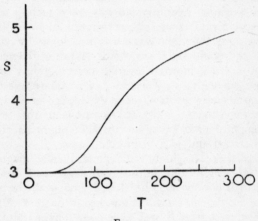

Fig. 15

Variation with the absolute temperature T of $s \; (= 2c_v, \; \div \; k/m)$ for hydrogen.

is why hydrogen's rotations and carbon dioxide's vibrations should suffer a disproportionately large decrease in energy as compared with the translatory motions.

Electrons and Atoms

Those who first realized these difficulties hoped that they would be resolved when more was known about the inside of a molecule. A clear picture of a molecule's make-up began to emerge in the first few years of this century.

A number of well-known facts indicate that a close relation exists between molecular properties and electricity. Chemical reactions are often caused by the flow of electricity through a solution, as in electroplating; a chemical reaction in a cell enables this to supply an electric current; and most bodies, solid or liquid, seriously affect an electric field in which they are placed. The reason has been found to be that molecules are made up of parts carrying electric charges.

In 1897, J. J. Thomson and Wiechert isolated an "atom" of negative electricity, the electron, a particle whose mass was less than a thousandth part of that of the lightest atom known. Following up this, Rutherford showed that the chemical atoms are not atoms in the Greek sense of indivisible particles. He found that any chemical atom can be divided up into a nucleus, containing most of the atom's mass, and a group of electrons. The nucleus has a positive electric charge, and in the normal state of the atom is surrounded by enough electrons exactly to balance its charge. The whole atom may be pictured as a sort of solar system, with the nucleus as sun and the electrons as planets; as in our solar system, the nucleus and planetary electrons are tiny compared with the total extent of the system. Molecules may similarly be likened to double or multiple stars, each star of the system possessing its own planets.

The apparent size of a molecule is due to the forces which its nuclei and electrons are able to exert on those of other molecules while yet some way off. The electrons form the outworks of an atom, beyond which no assailant can penetrate without tremendous energy; these outworks determine the everyday outward behaviour of the atom, like its chemical properties, or the force which it exerts on another atom. Atoms have been found with the same outworks, but possessing nuclei with different masses, though identical charges. Such atoms, possessing identical chemical properties, but different atomic weights, are called isotopes of each other. Thus, for example, the heavy hydrogen which gained such notoriety in connection with the atomic bomb is an isotope of the more usual hydrogen, and has atoms twice as heavy.

If an atom or molecule is bombarded by very fast particles, or illuminated by ultra-violet light, an electron may be knocked clean out of the atom, and become a free electron. The atom or molecule is then left with insufficient negative electrons to balance the positive charge of the nuclei, and is said to be ionized, or to be a positive ion. Certain types of atom or molecule are able to pick up free electrons, and so acquire one more electron than the normal quota; when they do so, they are called negative ions.

Rutherford's picture of an atom as a miniature solar system made it no easier to explain away the equipartition difficulty. If two atoms in a molecule are just loose structures, held together by the forces between them, there is nothing to prevent vibrations of one atom relative to the other; likewise many other sorts of vibration should be possible, in which the electrons take part.

Again, if the electrons in an atom have to travel round the nucleus, their motion is a sort of rotation of the atom. It is not the sort of rotation considered earlier, because the moment of inertia is not constant; it may not obey the equipartition law exactly, but it should certainly contribute to the total heat. There is no escape from the conclusion that if energy within an atom behaves like energy outside there is a complete contradiction between theory and experiment. Something within the atom must prevent its energy from behaving like energy outside. And so, even before Rutherford's picture was complete, new laws of the behaviour of an atom were being proposed by Planck, Einstein and Bohr.

The specific heat depends not on the total energy, but on the way in which this energy alters as the temperature increases. Thus the unexpected lowness of the specific heat does not mean that the molecules cannot rotate, or vibrate internally, but that they cannot change their energy freely. The new laws that were proposed asserted that the possible motions inside a molecule are restricted. The electrons travelling in planetary orbits round a nucleus cannot move in any arbitrary path: only a definite set of orbits are open to them. The possible energies of a particular vibration in a molecule are not unrestricted: they can take only certain definite values roughly equal to 0, E, $2E$, $3E$, ..., where E is a definite constant for the particular vibration considered, but varies from one vibration to another. All rates of rotation of a molecule are not possible: for example, the possible energies of rotation of a diatomic molecule are roughly 0, $2E'$, $6E'$, ..., $n(n + 1) E'$, ... where E' depends on the molecule.

When an atom or a molecule changes its energy, its particles—electrons or atoms—jump from one permitted motion to another. The process whereby the jump is accomplished is hard to conceive, and in these days even atomic physicists do not attempt to picture it. Electrons and atomic nuclei have been found to possess some of the properties of waves, and they must be regarded as very "fuzzy" particles, whose behaviour cannot be pictured like that of the masses which we can see. The lighter the particle, the greater is the fuzziness; an electron is the fuzziest, and indeed the picture of an atom as a solar system is nearly blurred out by the fuzz round the electrons. But even molecules as a whole have some degree of fuzziness, particularly light ones at low temperatures; possibly some of the softness of hydrogen and helium, which was mentioned in Chapter VII, is really due simply to this fuzziness.

The Failure of Equipartition

Experiment has now amply confirmed the suggestion that the internal energy of a molecule cannot alter arbitrarily, but only by definite amounts. The amounts by which the energy changes are called quanta (from the Latin word quantum = quantity, much used in doctors' prescriptions). In terms of quanta, the breakdown of equipartition can easily be explained.

In Chapter II, equipartition of translatory energy was compared with communism in a primitive society, none of whose members cared in the least how much or how little they possessed. In such a society, any individual might at one instant possess very little, and later, by a series of happy chances, acquire a great deal; averaging over a long time, however, each individual would have just as much as any other.

Suppose now that, in such a society, some individuals decide that they will never accept or give anything other than a pound note, or its equivalent, while still not caring whether they possess much or little. If the society is rich, and each possesses many pounds, this will hardly incommode them; they will usually find the people they meet able and willing to pass over a pound, and will possess much the same amount as the rest. But if the society is poor, and only a few have as much

H

as a pound at any time, their insistence on a "quantum" of one pound is likely to leave them in poverty; they have few chances of acquiring a pound, and are likely to find it taken from them quickly by a neighbour when they do get it.

It is like this with the molecules in a gas. When two molecules collide, one of them may be set vibrating; but as the possible energies of vibration are E, $2E$, $3E$, ..., this can happen only if the total energy of the molecules exceeds E. Actually, since it is unlikely that the whole energy of the molecules can go into a single vibration, the vibration is not likely to be set going unless E is much less than the whole energy of the colliding molecules. If E is large, a vibrating molecule is not likely to get its vibrational energy increased by a collision, but is quite likely to lose any that it may chance to possess. Thus, when E is large, few molecules can be vibrating at all at any special time, and there is very little vibrational energy about. When E is small, on the other hand molecules are easily set vibrating, and the mean energy of the vibrations is not very different from that given by equipartition. Similarly when the rotational quantum E' is small there is nearly equipartition of rotational and other energy but when it is large the molecules are nearly unable to rotate.

The quantum of energy is largest, generally speaking, when it refers to light particles. That is why monatomic gases appear not to rotate; the only rotation they could possess would be the rotation due to the orbits of electrons round the nucleus. The electrons get a basic ration of energy, else they would not be able to travel round the nucleus at all; but their energy cannot increase above the basic level, because it would take far too great a quantum of energy. Since the specific heat depends only on the way the energy increases with temperature, the rotations do not affect it. It is for the same reason that a diatomic molecule does not appear to rotate about the line joining the two nuclei; rotation about this line would likewise be due solely to the motions of electrons in their orbits.

As the temperature increases, more energy becomes available; the quantum of energy becomes smaller in proportion to the available energy, and equipartition is more nearly realized. This is why the specific heat of carbon dioxide increases as the temperature rises; at ordinary temperatures the energy available is not enough to permit the molecules to vibrate, but as the temperature increases more and more of them are set vibrating faster and faster. Conversely, as the temperature goes down, the energy available becomes less and less able to supply a large quantum of energy; this is why hydrogen stops rotating at low temperatures. The quantum of energy is smaller for gases other than hydrogen, and so a similar cessation of rotation is hardly noticeable in other diatomic gases.

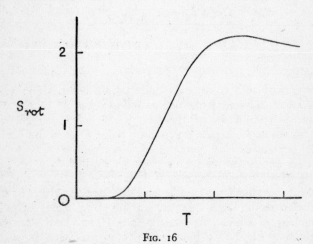

FIG. 16

Variation with the absolute temperature T of the rotational part of s ($= 2c_v$, $\div k/m$) for an ideal gas.

It is possible to calculate how the specific heat of a gas must vary with the temperature. The calculation cannot be given here, for it depends on the peculiar laws governing the inside of a molecule, which have only been hinted at in the preceding pages. The general form of the results can, however, be seen from Fig. 16, which shows the way in which the rotational part of the specific heat varies with temperature in an ideal diatomic gas.

Atomic theory, and even the study of specific heats, has by now gone far beyond such ideas as were first developed in studying gases. Maxwell would have been surprised to have

seen how far his mildly expressed dissatisfaction with current
ideas has led. Nevertheless, the principle of equipartition,
though now "cribbed, cabined, and confined", has had its
share, and this no mean one, in leading to the foundation
of wider studies, and to this extent gas theory has been fruitful
far outside its own proper boundaries.

CHAPTER IX

THE LAWS OF LARGE NUMBERS

Averages

THE density of a continuous body whose composition varies
from point to point is defined as follows. Let M be the mass
within a volume V of the body; the value which M/V
approaches as V shrinks up round a point P gives the density
at P.

This definition cannot usefully be applied to a gas consisting of separate molecules; if V is very small, at most one
molecule can be found in V, and the density given by this
definition would be a quantity varying from point to point,
being large if a molecule actually is at P, and zero otherwise.

Such a rapidly varying quantity is not what is usually
understood as the density of the gas. The density is usually
regarded as a quantity which varies smoothly throughout a
volume containing many molecules; it must be defined as M/V,
where V is a fairly small volume, which nevertheless contains
so many molecules that the accidental variations in position of
individual molecules can be neglected. This definition is, of
course, that assumed in experimental work. The density of
population in a particular part of a big city—so many per
square mile—has to be defined in much the same way.

A process like this, smoothing out the individual peculiarities of the molecules, has had to be used many times in
earlier chapters. In defining the pressure which a gas exerts
on the vessel enclosing it—a pressure which may vary from
time to time or from point to point of the vessel—we do not

think of the force being exerted at a given instant on a particular point of the vessel. A small area S of the vessel is taken
round a special point P, and the collisions of molecules with S
during a short time t are considered. It is supposed that
S and t are so small that, even if the pressure is different at
different points of the gas, or is changing as the time passes,
no appreciable differences in pressure are to be met at different
points of S, or from instant to instant of t; on the other hand,
S and t are so large that many molecules collide with S during
t, and the variations in the total momentum which they transfer to S, due to accidental fluctuations in the number of
molecules striking S, can be ignored.

Again, the temperature of a gas may vary from point to
point, or from time to time, but this difficulty equally cannot
be overcome by considering a special point and a special time.
The temperature is given by the average kinetic energy of a
large number of molecules; the average must be taken over
a volume which, though small, none the less contains enough
molecules for their individual peculiarities to be averaged out.

Each of these definitions depends on the assumption that
individual peculiarities can, in fact, be averaged out if only
averages are taken over a sufficient number of individuals. This
is an assumption regularly made in statistical work, and finding
a clear justification there. A fire usually, at least, occurs by
accident, and is unpredictable; nevertheless, fire insurance
companies find it possible to predict fairly accurately the
number of fires which will occur in a year or two. A doctrine
known as economic determinism is upheld in Marxist quarters;
this claims that men's actions are motivated by their economic
circumstances. It would be out of place here to argue whether
this doctrine is correct or not; but whether it is correct or not,
statistics are likely to show the behaviour of men in general
to be largely determined by economic motives. For, though
different men may be swayed by very different motives, and
only a few of these may be economic in origin, in the behaviour
of large numbers of men accidental variations from man to
man are cancelled out, and only those motives which affect
large numbers are important.

Though experience in statistical work does show that
individual peculiarities can usually be averaged out by taking

averages over large numbers, it remains theoretically possible that in special circumstances all one's expectations may be upset. In a gas, the density may from time to time prove unexpectedly "lumpy", and so on. It is possible to investigate exactly what fluctuations in density, etc., are likely to occur in a gas because of the random motions of the molecules, and this we proceed to do.

Uniformity of Density

When gas molecules move about in a closed vessel, each molecule is able to penetrate each corner of the vessel, and will actually do so if the gas is left to itself for a sufficiently long time. Suppose that the volume V of the vessel is divided into s equal parts, and that there is nothing, like differences in temperature, to distinguish one part from any other. Then, at a particular instant of a long time, any special molecule is just as likely to be in one of these parts as in any other. If v denotes one of these parts, we say that there is a probability $1/s$ that the molecule is in v; this means that, if the gas is examined at a large number of instants scattered through a long time, at $1/s$ of these instants it will be in v. The probability that it is not in v is similarly $1 - 1/s$.

The probability that a given molecule is in v is slightly altered if a second molecule is already known to be in v. The first molecule is then excluded from a part of v, since it cannot occupy the same volume as the second; on the other hand, since molecules tend to cling together, the first molecule shows a preference for the immediate vicinity of the second. Effects like these are important only when the deviations from Boyle's law are also important. They are neglected in what follows; that is, the probability that a given molecule is in v is supposed to be $1/s$, no matter how many other molecules are also in v.

Let x_r be a number associated with the rth of the N molecules inside V, defined to be such that $x_r = 1$ when the molecule is inside v, and $x_r = 0$ when it is not. Denote averages over a long time by a bar drawn over the corresponding symbol; then $\bar{x}_r$, the average of x_r, is $1/s$; and since $(x_r - 1/s)^2$ is $(1 - 1/s)^2$ for $1/s$ of the time, and $1/s^2$ for the rest, its average value is

$$\overline{\left(x_r - \frac{1}{s}\right)^2} = \frac{1}{s}\left(1 - \frac{1}{s}\right)^2 + \left(1 - \frac{1}{s}\right)\frac{1}{s^2}$$

$$= \frac{1}{s}\left(1 - \frac{1}{s}\right).$$

Again, if p and r are different, then because x_r and x_p are independent of each other,

$$\overline{\left(x_r - \frac{1}{s}\right)\left(x_p - \frac{1}{s}\right)} = \overline{\left(x_r - \frac{1}{s}\right)} \times \overline{\left(x_p - \frac{1}{s}\right)} = 0.$$

The sum of all the x's, $\sum x_r$, is the total number R of molecules in v; the average value of R is

$$\bar{R} = \sum x_r = N\bar{x}_r = N/s,$$

which is, of course, the value when the N molecules are evenly spread through the whole volume V.

As a measure of the extent to which R may fluctuate about its mean value N/s, we calculate the mean value of $(R - N/s)^2$. This is σ^2, where

$$\sigma^2 = \overline{\left(R - \frac{N}{s}\right)^2} = \overline{\left\{\left(x_1 - \frac{1}{s}\right) + \left(x_2 - \frac{1}{s}\right) + \left(x_3 - \frac{1}{s}\right) + \dots\right\}^2}$$

$$= \overline{\left(x_1 - \frac{1}{s}\right)^2} + \overline{\left(x_2 - \frac{1}{s}\right)^2} + \dots\dots$$

$$+ 2\overline{\left(x_1 - \frac{1}{s}\right)\left(x_2 - \frac{1}{s}\right)} + 2\overline{\left(x_1 - \frac{1}{s}\right)\left(x_3 - \frac{1}{s}\right)} + \dots\dots$$

$$= N\overline{\left(x_1 - \frac{1}{s}\right)^2}$$

$$= N\frac{1}{s}\left(1 - \frac{1}{s}\right).$$

The quantity σ measures the average amount by which R deviates from its mean value N/s; it is called the standard deviation of R from its mean. Thus the standard deviation increases with N, being proportional to $\sqrt{N}$. On the other hand, expressed as a fraction of the average number N/s of molecules in v, the deviations become less important as N increases; the ratio of σ to N/s is

$$\sqrt{\left\{\frac{N}{s}\left(1 - \frac{1}{s}\right)\right\}} \Big/ \frac{N}{s} = \sqrt{\left(\frac{s-1}{---}\right)}$$

and so is small if N/s is large.

The result just obtained is that, if N independent systems each have a probability $1/s$ of possessing a certain property, the fraction of them which actually possess this property is likely to deviate from N/s by an amount proportional to $1/\sqrt{N}$. This is a general result in the theory of statistics, known as the $\sqrt{N}$ law. It indicates that the accuracy of an average increases with the number of systems—roughly speaking, that individual peculiarities can be averaged out if an average is taken over enough systems. A fire insurance company can predict reasonably accurately what fraction of those insured with it will submit *bona fide* claims for insurance in a few years, provided simply that the total number of claims concerned is large.

In gases, the numbers of molecules present are so large that fluctuations about mean values are extremely small. Suppose, for example, that a volume of gas at N.T.P. is divided into a very large number of smaller volumes, each equal to the volume of a cube of edge 0·01 cm. The probable number of molecules, N/s, in any of these smaller volumes is $2·7 \times 10^{13}$. The probable fluctuation of density in one of the smaller volumes, measured as a fraction of the average density, is roughly $\sqrt{(s/N)}$, or 2×10^{-7} of the whole. Such a fluctuation can usually be completely disregarded.

The Error Law

However, although the departures from uniformity of density must be very small for most of the time, it still remains possible that much larger departures may occur for short times. It is interesting to know how often this is likely to occur—how often, say, the deviation of the number R of molecules in v from the mean value is five or ten times the standard deviation σ. To ascertain this, the probability that R takes exactly some particular value has to be calculated.

Suppose that the probabilities of two independent events are P and P'. Then in a fraction P of a large number of trials the first event will occur, and in a fraction P' of these the second also occurs. Thus in a fraction PP' of the trials both events occur; that is, the probability of both occurring together is PP'. Similarly, if the probabilities of N independent events are $P_1, P_2, \ldots P_N$, the probability that they all occur together is $P_1 P_2 P_3 \ldots \ldots P_N$. In particular, the probability that, of the N molecules in V, R *special* ones are, at a particular instant, in v, and the remaining $N - R$ are elsewhere, is

$$\left(\frac{1}{s}\right)^R \left(1 - \frac{1}{s}\right)^{N-R}$$

This is not the total probability that, of the N molecules, just R are in v; the R special ones to go into v can be picked in a large number of ways from the N—to be exact, in

$$\frac{N!}{R!(N-R)!}$$

ways, where $N! = 1 \cdot 2 \cdot 3 \ldots . N$. Thus the total probability of finding just R molecules in v is $P(R)$, where

$$P(R) = \frac{N!}{R!(N-R)!}\left(\frac{1}{s}\right)^R \left(1 - \frac{1}{s}\right)^{N-R} . \quad . \quad (39)$$

The way in which $P(R)$ varies with R is illustrated by "frequency-diagrams" in Fig. 17, for the case $s = 3$, with $N = 12$, 27 and 75. The heights of the vertical ordinates represent the values of $P(R)$ for the different values of R; the scales of these heights in the three diagrams are adjusted to make the maximum height (that for $R = N/s$) the same in each diagram. Not all possible values of R are illustrated, but only those for which $P(R)$ is appreciable; the difference between the greatest and least values of R illustrated is $4\sqrt{(\frac{1}{3}N)}$ in each diagram. The spread of the ordinates about the maximum ordinate is much the same in the three diagrams; that is, the ordinate whose height is any definite fraction of the greatest height comes at about the same place in each diagram. It is the spread of the ordinates which is measured by the standard deviation σ; since the horizontal scales of the diagrams are proportional to $1/\sqrt{N}$, the fact that the diagrams each show much the same spread implies that σ is proportional to $\sqrt{N}$, as was proved in last section.

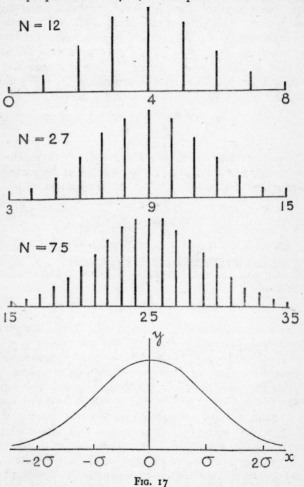

FIG. 17

Variation of $P\,(R)$ with R for $N = 12$, 27 and 75, taking $s = 3$
The curve at the foot is the error curve.

Suppose that the values of $P(R)$ for increasing values of N, and the same s, are drawn on a succession of frequency-diagrams like those of Fig. 17. Suppose also that, as in Fig. 17, the vertical scale is adjusted to make the maximum ordinate the same in all the diagrams, and that the horizontal scale is proportional to $1/\sqrt{N}$. Then, as Fig. 17 illustrates, the smooth curve drawn through the tops of the ordinates tends to a definite limiting form as N becomes large, the limiting form being that shown in the last diagram in Fig. 17. The proof of this will not be given here; but the limiting curve can be shown to be the "error curve" whose equation, referred to appropriate co-ordinate axes, is

$$y = \frac{1}{\sqrt{(2\pi)}\,\sigma}\, e^{-\frac{1}{2}x^2/\sigma^2} \qquad . \qquad . \qquad . \qquad (40)$$

where e is the base of Napierian logarithms, $2.718 \ldots$. The abscissa x in this is $R - N/s$; the ordinate y is the same as $P(R)$.

When N is large, $P(R)$ need not be calculated for all values of R, since $P(R)$ does not vary greatly from one value of R to the next. Instead, a long succession of nearly equal values of $P(R)$ are grouped together. Let such a succession extend from $R = R_1$ to $R = R_2$; $R_2 - R_1$ is a large number, and, if R lies between R_1 and R_2, $P(R)$ is nearly equal to $P(R_1)$. Thus the probability that R lies between R_1 and R_2 is

$$(R_2 - R_1)\, P(R_1).$$

If $R = R_1$ and $R = R_2$ correspond to $x = x_1$, $y = y_1$ and $x = x_2$, $y = y_2$ on the error curve, this is

$$(x_2 - x_1)\, y_1$$

which equals the area under the error curve between the ordinates at $x = x_1$ and $x = x_2$. That is, the probability that R lies between two assigned values equals the area under the error curve between two appropriate ordinates. The result has been proved only when $P(R)$ varies little between $R = R_1$ and $R = R_2$; but, by adding the results for a succession of ranges in each of which $P(R)$ varies little, the result can be seen to be generally true. In particular, since the total probability of R taking all possible values is obviously unity, the total area under the error curve is unity.

The probability that R should deviate from its mean value N/s by more than, say, q times the standard deviation σ is now seen to be the total area under the error-curve outside the ordinates at $x = \pm q\,\sigma$. For $q = 2$, this is 0·045; for $q = 5$, it is less than a millionth; for $q = 10$, it is enormously small—less than 10^{-22}. Thus, while it is theoretically possible for large fluctuations of density to occur in a small volume of a gas, their probability is very small. Suppose, as before, that a volume of gas at N.T.P. is divided up into a very large number of parts, each equal in volume to a cube of edge 0·01 cm. Taking $q = 5$, a fluctuation amounting to millionth of the average density is to be expected only for a total time amounting to less than a second in ten days; a fluctuation twice as big would be expected for only a millionth of a second, all told, in the time since the Earth was first formed.

Normal Properties

A property which, in any given state of a gas, is very nearly attained for very nearly all the time, is called a normal property of the gas. In this sense, uniformity of density is a normal property of the gas which has just been considered. There are many other normal properties. Uniformity of temperature can be shown to be a normal property of a gas left to itself. Similarly, in any steady flow of gas, the velocity at any point is a normal property; when different parts of a gas are maintained at different temperatures, the temperature at any point is a normal property. A normal property would be an actual property but for the fact that the gas consists of molecules each with its own individuality.

The results just obtained for the density clearly suggest that, for most purposes, normal properties can be treated as if they were actual properties; they are, in fact, so treated by physicists in experiments on gas in bulk. The number of molecules in any actual gas is so enormous that their individual properties can be averaged out.

Large deviations from a normal property are not theoretically impossible. Suppose, for example, that half of a mass of gas is hotter than the other half. The fast-moving molecules in the hotter half tend to travel into the cooler half, and the slower molecules in the cooler half tend to travel into the warmer half, until ultimately all the gas contains the same proportions of fast and slow molecules, and the gas is in a uniform state. Suppose now that at a certain instant the velocities of all the molecules are exactly reversed; then each molecule retraces its steps, until at last the original state, with half the gas hotter than the other half, is recovered. That is, starting from a state in which its properties are indistinguishable from normal properties, the gas has attained a very different state.

In practice, gas never does actually sort itself out in this way into two halves at different temperatures. The process of such sorting, while possible, is enormously improbable; it can, moreover, be completely spoilt by giving a single molecule a slightly incorrect velocity at the start, or by slightly jolting the vessel containing the gas. Thus, if a gas is left to itself, its properties never diverge very far from normal properties.

Of course, this state of affairs could be upset by intelligence. Maxwell imagined a "sorting demon" who could watch each molecule as it moved about, and so could divide gas into hotter and cooler parts. He supposed that a vessel containing gas "is divided into two portions A and B, by a division in which there is a small hole, and that a being, who can see the individual molecules, opens and closes this hole, so as to allow only the swifter molecules to pass from A to B, and the slower ones to pass from B to A. He will thus without expenditure of work, raise the temperature of B and lower that of A". The distinction between the workings of intelligence and chance is clearly illustrated in this example; by no means is it possible scientifically to explain intelligence as the outcome of a favourable set of accidents to each of a large number of disconnected systems.

One may ask if some machine might not be invented which, like the calculating machine called the "electronic brain", would behave as if it had some degree of intelligence, and work like Maxwell's demon. If the division between the parts A and B of the gas were a membrane which let only fast molecules pass through it in one direction, and slow molecules pass through it in the other, this could replace the sorting demon; could not such a membrane be found? The answer is that, while such a membrane is perhaps not theoretically impossible, the only way in which it could test whether a gas-molecule is fast or slow would be by letting that molecule strike one of its own molecules, and this would alter the energy of the gas-molecule and so upset the sorting.

More refined ways of replacing Maxwell's demon could be found, but they would almost certainly demand a greater expenditure of power that the direct heating of one part of the gas and cooling of the other.

Without the intervention of intelligence, a mass of gas always travels "downhill" to a state where its properties are normal properties; "accidents" (large deviations from the normal state) simply do not occur in the average of a large number of systems operating blindly and independently. As mentioned earlier, a doctrine of economic determinism might be constructed by regarding men as similar to molecules, all their individual peculiarities being wiped out in considering the behaviour of men in bulk, which has only "normal" properties. The analogy is, however, imperfect, since men are not independent units to the extent that gas-molecules are. For example, during the latter half of the nineteenth century, unemployment went up and down regularly in cycles lasting about nine years, even though there was no very obvious material cause of these fluctuations. The reason seems to have been that the confidence of many employers and purchasers waxed and waned simultaneously, in response to the spirit about at the time. Effects of communal thinking like these have no counterpart in the properties of gases.

Distribution Functions

Suppose that the members of a large population—e.g. people of a special country, or molecules in a particular mass of gas—possess a certain measurable characteristic X—the height of the people, or the energy of the molecules. Consider those members of the population, S in number, for which X has values between x and $x + \delta x$. The quantity δx can be taken to be small compared with the total spread of values of X, and yet so large that S is a large number. If x is fixed, and δx varies (though always remaining small), S is roughly proportional to δx. It would be exactly proportional to δx, were it not that the population considered, though large, is finite, and the individual peculiarities of the members have to be taken into account. But, since S is large, fluctuations in it due to these peculiarities produce a relatively small effect. Neglecting them, we can put

$$S = f(x) \times \delta x.$$

The function $f(x)$ defined in this manner is called the distribution function of the property X. It is a normal property of the population, in the sense defined above. The area under the curve $y = f(x)$ between the ordinates at x and $x + \delta x$ is $f(x) \times \delta x$, i.e. S; the area under it between any two ordinates $x = x_1$ and $x = x_2$ is similarly the number of members of the population for which X takes values between x_1 and x_2.

The distribution function can be used in calculating mean values like $\overline{X}$, the mean value of X for the whole population, or the mean value of $(X - \overline{X})^2$, which gives σ^2, the square of the standard deviation of values of X from their mean $\overline{X}$. For example, the sum of the values of X for members of the set S just considered is xS, or

$$xf(x)\, \delta x.$$

Summation over sets like S, covering all possible values of X, gives the sum of the X's for the whole population; and this is $P\overline{X}$, where P is the total number in the population.

A particular form of distribution function was defined incidentally just now. Let the population P represent P observations of the gas in the volume V, made at intervals during a long time, and let R be the number of molecules in the sub-volume v in any observation. Then the distribution function for R in the set of observations is P times the error function defined earlier; that is, it is

$$f(x) = P \cdot \frac{1}{\sqrt{(2\,\pi)}\,\sigma} e^{-(x-\bar{x})^2/2\sigma^2} \qquad \cdot \quad \cdot \quad \cdot \quad (41)$$

where $x = R$, $\bar{x} = N/s$. Distribution functions like that given by (41) are often encountered in practice; P is the number of members in the population considered (in the case just mentioned, a "population" of different observations), $\bar{x}$ is the mean of the values of x, and σ, the standard deviation, measures the degree of spread of the values of x about their mean value. A distribution given by (41) is called a "normal", or "Gaussian" distribution (after the German mathematician Gauss).

A Gaussian distribution arises whenever the deviation of x from its mean value $\bar{x}$ is due to a large number of independent causes, any of which may introduce a small deviation, just as likely to be positive as negative. For example, the heights of grown men of a particular race are distributed roughly according to a Gaussian law; the independent causes here are different factors of heredity and environment. In a large number of measurements of a given physical quantity, the errors of the separate measures may often be regarded as arising from a large number of unrelated causes; when this is so, the measures are distributed round the true value in a Gaussian distribution. It is this connection with error distributions that gives the error curve its name. In the gas problem considered earlier, the molecules provided N independent causes of possible deviations of R from N/s, whence the Gaussian distribution of R.

The distribution function $f(x)$ depends on a single variable x; distribution functions can also be found which depend on more than one variable. Suppose that x and y are two distinct measurable characteristics possessed by every member of a population—like the height and weight of a man, or the energies of translation and rotation of a gas molecule. The population is supposed to be so numerous that, even when δx and δy are both relatively small, the number S of members of the population such that the first characteristic has a value between x and $x + \delta x$, and the other a value between y and $y + \delta y$, is large. If x, y are fixed and δx, δy vary, S is roughly proportional to $\delta x \times \delta y$; we write

$$S = f(x, y)\, \delta x\, \delta y.$$

Then $f(x, y)$ is a distribution function representing the distribution of both x and y among the population.

What $f(x, y)$ means can be illustrated graphically as follows. Every member of the population can be represented by a point in a plane, the x and y co-ordinates of the point being the values of x and y for that member (see Fig. 18). According to our assumption, there are so many points that, even in an area small compared with the total scatter, a large number of points are found—at least in the denser parts of the diagram. The distribution function $f(x, y)$ gives the number of points per unit area near the point x, y of the diagram. The curves $f(x, y) =$ constant are something like isobars of the diagram— they are curves of constant density of the points. In Fig. 18, these would be circles.

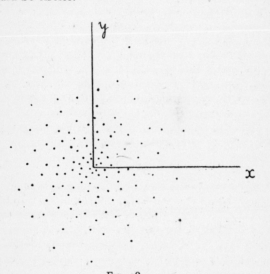

FIG. 18

Scatter diagram illustrating a distribution function $f(x, y)$ depending on two variables x and y.

Sometimes the distribution of y among the population depends on the value of x; for example, if x is a man's height, y his weight, large values of y tend to accompany large values of x. On the other hand, if x is a man's height, y the number of words he speaks in a day, x and y should be unrelated. In the latter case, the distributions of x and y are independent, and, just as the joint probability of two unrelated events is the product of their separate probabilities, $f(x, y)$ can be put in the form $f_1(x) \times f_2(y)$. This case is that illustrated in Fig. 18,

I

taking f_1 and f_2 to be Gaussian functions with the same standard deviation. As Maxwell pointed out, a diagram like Fig. 18 resembles the pattern of shots fired at a target; the marksman actually makes his own distribution diagram, x and y being the deviations, sideways and up, of his aim from the bull's-eye.

Velocity-distributions.

The distribution functions used in studying gases mostly depend on three or more variables. One of them, which has often been used already, is the number-density, or number of molecules per unit volume. To define this correctly, we should have to say that it is n, where nV is the number of molecules in a volume V which, though small, is large enough to contain many molecules. In a non-uniform gas, it depends on the co-ordinates (x, y, z) of the point considered. To make its definition run parallel to that of the two-dimensional distribution function $f(x, y)$, the volume V is taken to be a rectangular block with small edges δx, δy, and δz parallel to the co-ordinate axes; then the number of molecules in the block is

$$S = n \, \delta x \, \delta y \, \delta z.$$

Consider now the n molecules in unit volume of a uniform gas. Select from these molecules the set, S' in number, whose component velocities parallel to Ox, Oy and Oz lie respectively between u and $u + \delta u$, v and $v + \delta v$, and w and $w + \delta w$; in the usual way, δu, δv, δw are supposed to be small compared with the total spread of the velocities, but large enough for S' to be a large number. If

$$S' = f(u, v, w)\delta u \delta v \delta w$$

the function $f(u, v, w)$ is called the velocity-distribution function. It depends on the three variables $u, v,$ and w; it would also have to depend on position if the gas were non-uniform.

The velocity-distribution function can itself be represented as a number-density, as follows. Each molecule of the n in unit volume can be represented by a point P, whose co-ordinates are the components u, v, w of the velocity $\mathbf{c}$ of the molecule. If O is the origin of co-ordinates, OP represents $\mathbf{c}$ in magnitude and direction. The number S' is the number of representative points P in a rectangular block with edges δu, δv, δw, and so

$f(u, v, w)$ is the number-density of the representative points near the point whose co-ordinates are u, v, w. Like n, the function $f(u, v, w)$ is a normal property of the gas, not an actual property; that is, S' is equal to $f(u, v, w) \, \delta u \, \delta v \, \delta w$ only if small accidental fluctuations, due to the obstinate individuality of the molecules, are smoothed out.

Few molecules have speeds more than three or four times the average speed $\bar{c}$. Hence the representative points P form a sort of cluster or cloud, dense near the centre, but thinning out rapidly at its edges. From a long way off, the cloud would be seen as if it all lay in a plane perpendicular to the line of sight, and would look rather like that shown in Fig. 18. The centre of the cloud is at the origin if the gas as a whole is at rest, but is at a rather different point if the gas is moving bodily in any direction.

The velocity-distribution function is very important in any accurate theory of viscosity, heat conduction, etc. The accurate values of the viscosity and other similar quantities are, in fact, calculated by first finding this function.

CHAPTER X

MAXWELL'S LAW

The Uniform Steady State

SUPPOSE that a quantity of gas, uniform in density and temperature, is in a vessel whose temperature is the same as that of the gas. As time passes, the gas remains in the same state; it can be said to be in a uniform steady state.

The velocity-distribution function in this state was first determined by Maxwell. It is

$$f(u, v, w) = \frac{n}{\{\sqrt{(2\pi)}\sigma\}^3} \, e^{-c^2/2\sigma^2} \qquad . \quad . \quad (42)$$

where, as usual, $c^2 = u^2 + v^2 + w^2$.

Equation (42) implies that, if δu, δv and δw are fairly small, the number of molecules per unit volume with velocity-components between u and $u + \delta u$, v and $v + \delta v$, and w and $w + \delta w$ is

$$f(u, v, w)\, \delta u\, \delta v\, \delta w = n \times \frac{1}{\sqrt{(2\pi)}\sigma} e^{-u^2/2\sigma^2}\, \delta u$$

$$\times \frac{1}{\sqrt{(2\pi)}\sigma} e^{-v^2/2\sigma^2}\, \delta v$$

$$\times \frac{1}{\sqrt{(2\pi)}\sigma} e^{-w^2/2\sigma^2}\, \delta w$$

Thus the distribution of values of u is completely independent of the values of v and w; it is a Gaussian distribution with standard deviation σ, about the mean value $\bar{u} = 0$. That is, the probability that the x-component of velocity lies between u and $u + \delta u$ is

$$\frac{1}{\sqrt{(2\pi)}\sigma} e^{-u^2/2\sigma^2}\, \delta u$$

whatever be the values of v and w. The distributions of v and w are similar.

Since σ is the standard deviation of each of u, v or w

$$\overline{u^2} = \overline{v^2} = \overline{w^2} = \sigma^2$$

Thus, since $\frac{1}{2} m\overline{u^2} = \frac{1}{2}kT$,

$$\sigma^2 = kT/m \qquad . \qquad . \qquad . \qquad . \qquad (43)$$

As mentioned earlier, if every molecule in unit volume of the gas is represented by a point P, such that OP gives the velocity **c** in magnitude and direction, $f(u, v, w)$ is the number-density of these points. Fig. 18 in fact showed exactly what the cloud of representative points would look like in a uniform steady state. Equation (42) shows that the density of these points depends only on the distance c from O; the maximum of density is at O, and there are very few points in any region where c is large compared with σ. The number of molecules with speeds between c and $c + \delta c$ is the number of points P between spheres, centre O, with radii c and $c + \delta c$. If δc is small, the volume between the spheres is roughly the area of one times the distance between the two, i.e. $4\pi c^2 \delta c$; thus the number of points P between the spheres is

$$4\pi c^2 \delta c \, \frac{n}{\{\sqrt{(2\pi)}\sigma\}^3} \, e^{-c^2/2\sigma^2}$$

That is, the distribution function for molecular *speeds* is $F(c)$, where

$$F(c) = 4\pi c^2 \frac{n}{\{\sqrt{(2\pi)}\sigma\}^3} \, e^{-c^2/2\sigma^2}$$

$$= n \sqrt{\left(\frac{2}{\pi}\right)} \frac{c^2}{\sigma^3} \, e^{-c^2/2\sigma^2} \qquad . \qquad . \qquad . \quad (44)$$

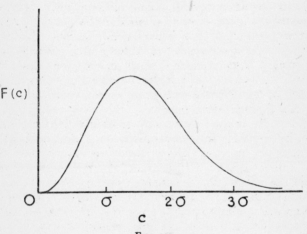

Fig. 19
Graph of $F(c)$ against c.

The graph of this function is shown in Fig. 19.

As explained in the last chapter, distribution functions can be used to determine mean values; thus equation (44) can be used to find mean values like $\bar{c}$, the mean speed of all the molecules. In fact, it gives

$$\bar{c} = \sqrt{\left(\frac{8}{\pi}\right)} \sigma.$$

Since

$$\overline{c^2} = \overline{u^2} + \overline{v^2} + \overline{w^2} = 3\sigma^2,$$

it follows that

$$\sqrt{(\overline{c^2})} = \sqrt{\left(\frac{3\pi}{8}\right)}\,\bar{c} = 1\cdot086\bar{c}.$$

a relation quoted earlier.

Combining (42) and (43), we see that $f(u, v, w)$ is proportional to $e^{-W/kT}$, where W is the total kinetic energy of translation of a molecule. Similarly the distribution-function for u alone is proportional to $e^{-W_1/kT}$, where W_1 is the kinetic energy of the x-motion, and so on.

Proofs of Maxwell's Law

Since the distribution of each of the component velocities is Gaussian, one might expect the proof of this distribution to be like the usual proof of a Gaussian distribution. This would mean that the x-component of velocity of a molecule would arise from a large number of small independent causes. But, in fact, the velocity of a molecule suffers a series of large changes at its collisions with other molecules; it cannot arise from small independent causes.

Maxwell's original derivation of his distribution function began by assuming that the distributions of u, v, and w among the molecules must be independent of each other. Also, since the number-density of the cloud of representative points cannot depend on the directions chosen for those of the co-ordinate axes, $f(u, v, w)$ must depend on u, v, and w only through the combination $c^2 = u^2 + v^2 + w^2$. Maxwell showed that equation (42) gives the only velocity-distribution consistent with these statements.

The weakness in this argument is the assumption that the distributions of u, v, and w are independent. There is no obvious reason why this should be so; a collision may, say, turn a velocity from the x-direction into the y-direction, and so the u, v, and w components of motion are mixed up inextricably in the equations governing a collision. Though Maxwell's argument did give the correct value of $f(u, v, w)$, this was by luck rather than desert.

Recognizing this, Maxwell attempted a second proof, based on the fact that $f(u, v, w)$ must be a function which is not altered by the collisions which are continually going on in the gas. He supposed the molecules to be smooth and round; they need not be hard, but may repel each other at a distance. When two molecules collide, let their velocities be c_1 and c_2 before the collision, and c'_1 and c'_2 after. Then an "inverse" collision is also possible, in which the velocities are c'_1 and c'_2 before collision, and c_1 and c_2 after. Inverse collisions like this are illustrated in Fig. 20. The velocity-changes which take place in the original, "direct" collision are gone through in

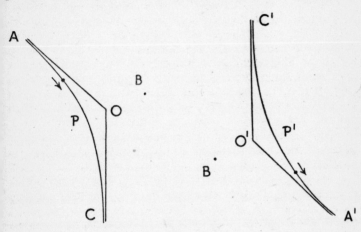

FIG. 20

The paths APC, $C'P'A'$ of one molecule relative to a second, B, in a direct collision and its inverse. The initial velocity in the direct collision (along AO) is the final velocity (along $O'A'$) in the inverse, and *vice versa*.

exactly the reverse order in the inverse collision. The total kinetic energy of the colliding molecules is unaltered in each collision, i.e.

$$\tfrac{1}{2}mc_1^2 + \tfrac{1}{2}mc_2^2 = \tfrac{1}{2}mc'_1{}^2 + \tfrac{1}{2}mc'_2{}^2.$$

Thus if $f(c)$ is used as an abbreviation for Maxwell's function (42),

$$f(c_1) \times f(c_2) = f(c'_1) \times f(c'_2) \quad . \quad . \quad (45)$$

Consider now all the collisions in which the initial velocities of the molecules are nearly equal to c_1 and c_2, and the final velocities are nearly equal to c'_1 and c'_2. The number of such collisions occurring per second in unit volume is proportional, among other things, to the numbers of molecules with velocities nearly equal to c_1 and c_2, which are available for collisions, and so is proportional to $f(c_1) \times f(c_2)$. The number of inverse collisions, in which the initial velocities are nearly equal to c'_1 and c'_2 and the final velocities are nearly equal to c_1 and c_2, occurring per second in unit volume, is similarly proportional to $f(c'_1) \times f(c'_2)$. The proportionality factor can be shown to be the same for direct and inverse collisions; hence (45) implies that the decrease in numbers of molecules with velocities nearly equal to c_1 and c_2 due to direct collisions is exactly balanced by the increase in numbers due to inverse collisions. This being so, collisions between molecules do not alter the number of molecules with velocities nearly equal to any value c, i.e. they do not affect $f(c)$. Thus Maxwell's velocity-distribution gives a state of the gas which is both uniform and steady.

This argument, again, is open to some criticism. Firstly, it assumes that the velocities of neighbouring molecules are unrelated; if they are related, the number of direct collisions is not exactly proportional to $f(c_1) \times f(c_2)$. The answer to this objection is that, unless the molecules cling together (as they do considerably in solids and liquids, but not very much in gases) the velocities of neighbouring molecules can only be related to an inappreciable extent. Two molecules may be neighbours at one instant, but each has come a relatively long distance since its last collision, and has travelled past many other molecules. The velocities of two molecules should be related only if one has exerted a definite influence on the other in the immediate past. Such an influence can be exerted only by both colliding in turn with a third molecule, and this is very unlikely to have actually occurred. In a dense gas, Maxwell's argument might conceivably need some correction, but at ordinary densities it appears to be sound.

A second criticism is that Maxwell's argument only shows that his velocity-distribution function gives one uniform steady state; there may conceivably be others. His function might conceivably correspond to a state which, though steady, was unstable and therefore improbable in an actual gas; the function sought is a very probable one—a normal property.

This criticism was met by Boltzmann (1872), who showed that Maxwell's function is the only possible one to give a uniform steady state, and that, except for the fluctuations due to the molecules' individuality, the velocity-distribution function in a gas left to itself always rapidly approaches Maxwell's function.

A third criticism is that an artificial model of a molecule is assumed. Any internal structure of a molecule is ignored; the translatory motions are supposed to be unaffected, at collisions, by the internal motions of rotation or vibration which the molecules may possess. This assumption is certainly incorrect for other than monatomic gases. If, however, internal motions do affect the course of a collision, no collision inverse to a given collision can in general be found, and so the argument breaks down. Boltzmann and Lorentz (1887) attempted to meet this objection in different ways, but their attempts, though not unsuccessful, lacked the simplicity of the earlier discussion.

In passing, it may be noted that Maxwell's argument leads to a second proof of the equipartition of translational kinetic energy between molecules of different masses. If two gases are mixed together, they have different velocity-distribution functions, f_1 and f_2, say; and in a steady state these satisfy a relation like (45), i.e.,

$$f_1(\mathbf{c}_1) \times f_2(\mathbf{c}_2) = f_1(\mathbf{c}'_1) \times f_2(\mathbf{c}'_2).$$

If f_1, f_2 are Maxwellian functions with different standard deviations σ_1 and σ_2, this implies that

$$\frac{c_1{}^2}{2\sigma_1{}^2} + \frac{c_2{}^2}{2\sigma_2{}^2} = \frac{c'_1{}^2}{2\sigma_1{}^2} + \frac{c'_2{}^2}{2\sigma_2{}^2}.$$

This equation follows from the constancy of kinetic energy at a collision only if

$$m_1\sigma_1{}^2 = m_2\sigma_2{}^2.$$

Now

$$\sigma_1{}^2 = \overline{u_1{}^2} = \overline{v_1{}^2} = \overline{w_1{}^2} = \tfrac{1}{3}\overline{c_1{}^2}, \text{ etc.,}$$

and so this implies that

$$\tfrac{1}{2}m_1\overline{c_1{}^2} = \tfrac{1}{2}m_2\overline{c_2{}^2},$$

which is the equipartition property quoted.

The statistical proof

Towards the end of last century, the growing difficulties about equipartition led to doubts about anything remotely connected with it. In particular, the objections to Maxwell's derivation of his velocity-distribution function were perhaps given greater weight than they deserved. To meet these objections, and provide a further proof of the equipartition law, Jeans, in 1903, gave a completely different and more general derivation. This, like the proof of the equipartition law given in Chapter II, simply considered how the total ration of energy must be divided among all the molecules claiming a share. The argument applies to molecules with any internal structure, but for simplicity we again consider only smooth round molecules with no detailed internal structure whatever.

If an unlimited supply of kinetic energy were available, the probability that a molecule has component velocities between u and $u + \delta u$, v and $v + \delta v$, and w and $w + \delta w$ would be the same for all values of u, v and w provided that δu, δv, and δw were kept constant. In actual fact, at a given temperature the molecules possess only a certain definite total amount of energy. This fact limits the energy which one single molecule can expect to possess; by itself it secures that the actual velocity-distribution has Maxwell's form.

To understand the line of argument, suppose that the x, y, and z component velocities of a molecule each can take only the values 0, $\pm \epsilon$, $\pm 2\epsilon$, $\pm 3 \epsilon, \cdots$. The unit ϵ is supposed to be fairly small compared with the mean velocity $\bar{c}$, so that the restriction on values of the velocity is not a really serious one. On the other hand, ϵ must not be taken too small. It is desired to be able to neglect the fluctuations due to the individuality of the molecules, and if too many values of the velocity are available very few molecules will possess any particular velocity.

The total kinetic energy of the molecules must be a multiple of the unit $E = \frac{1}{2}m\epsilon^2$, say QE. Suppose that this energy is divided among the molecules in such a way that each molecule receives a definite velocity, whose magnitude and direction are both assigned. This provides what we may call a rationing scheme for the molecules. All sets of velocities of the molecules giving the correct total energy are equally probable; that is, all rationing schemes are equally probable.

But this does not mean that all velocity-distribution functions are equally probable. In considering the velocity-distribution function we are not concerned with all the details of the rationing scheme; we need to know how many molecules possess any particular velocity, but not which molecules these are. A division of the total energy among the molecules such that an assigned number possess any particular velocity can be called a distribution of the energy. One distribution corresponds to a large number of different rationing schemes, since the actual molecules which possess a particular velocity can be chosen in a large number of different ways from the total number (N, say) of molecules present. All rationing schemes are equally probable, but all distributions are not; those distributions which correspond to very many rationing schemes are more probable than those which correspond to fewer.

For example, suppose that Q is of the form $4q^2$, where q is a whole number. Then one distribution of the total energy QE is to give it all to one molecule, giving this a velocity $2q\epsilon$ in the x-direction. This distribution corresponds to N distinct rationing schemes—the energy can be given to any one of the N molecules. A second distribution, a trifle less monopolistic than the first, is to divide the energy equally among four of the molecules, and to give the first a velocity $q\epsilon$ in the x-direction, the second a velocity $-q\epsilon$ in the same direction, and the third and fourth velocities $q\epsilon$ in the y- and z-directions. The first molecule could be chosen in N ways; the second is then chosen in $N-1$ ways from the remaining molecules; the third then in $N-2$ ways, and the fourth in $N-3$.

The new distribution therefore corresponds to $N(N-1)(N-2)(N-3)$ distinct rationing schemes. This is enormously greater than the number of rationing schemes corresponding to the first distribution, since N is a large number. Thus the second distribution is enormously more probable than the first; and other distributions, in which the energy is yet more evenly spread, are again far more probable still. When one molecule, or a few of the molecules, get far more than their fair share of energy, the distribution of the rest of the ration among the others is made far more difficult. A fairly uniform division of energy is far more probable than anything approaching a monopoly.

None the less, exact uniformity of energy is not the most probable state. Suppose, say, that the energy can be divided out in such a way that all molecules have the same energy, and all are moving parallel to Ox with the same velocity. This distribution corresponds to one and only one rationing scheme; there is nothing to distinguish one molecule from the other, and so the molecules are all picked in a lump, at once. Thus complete communism—all molecules equal—is even less probable than complete monopoly. The most probable distributions are those which correspond to the maximum possible diversity between the molecules consistent with no molecule having so much energy that it seriously handicaps the rest. True communism, like a monopolistic state, results only from intelligent planning; neither are to be expected in a gas, where a molecule is as ready to acquire as to surrender energy.

Clearly, then, certain distributions, intermediate between monopoly and communism, are far more probable than others. Jeans was able to prove that distributions differing only slightly from Maxwell's velocity-distribution are extremely probable; by comparison, distributions seriously differing from Maxwell's form are so improbable that the possibility of their appearance can be neglected. In an actual mass of gas, as the molecules move about, and collide with each other, the velocity-distribution function may fluctuate very slightly, but it always remains very close to Maxwell's function. That is, Maxwell's velocity-distribution function is a normal property of a gas in a uniform steady state.

Since Jeans's argument depended solely on the fact that a certain amount of energy had to be divided among the molecules it naturally led to a proof of the equipartition of kinetic energy between molecules of different mass. For molecules with internal structure, it similarly led to a proof of equipartition for internal energy, and quieted any lingering doubts that the disagreement with experiments on specific heat might be due to errors in theoretical method.

Other Distribution Functions.

Maxwell's function is

$$f(u, v, w) = \frac{n}{(\sqrt{(2\pi)}\sigma)^3} e^{-W/m\sigma^2}$$

$$= \frac{n}{(\sqrt{(2\pi)}\sigma)^3} e^{-W/kT} \qquad . \qquad . \qquad (46)$$

where W is the kinetic energy $\frac{1}{2}mc^2$ of a molecule. This result can be generalized in several ways.

First, suppose that the vessel containing the gas is made to move with the constant velocity $\mathbf{c}_0$. Then $f(u, v, w)$ still takes the form (46), but W is now the kinetic energy relative to the vessel—the kinetic energy that would be measured by an observer moving with the vessel, and unaware of its motion. When a molecule collides with the vessel, and bounces off, its energy relative to the vessel is unaltered, but its energy in space changes; thus $f(u, v, w)$ has now to be calculated from the fact that a given total energy *relative to the vessel* has to be distributed among the molecules. The new value of W is $\frac{1}{2}mC^2$, where $\mathbf{C}$ is the velocity relative to the vessel (given by the vector difference $\mathbf{c} - \mathbf{c}_0$).

Next, think of an atmosphere at rest under gravity, whose temperature is the same at all heights. The molecules in the atmosphere have potential energy as well as kinetic; at a height h above the ground, the potential energy of a molecule of weight mg is mgh. The total energy of a molecule now is

$$W = mgh + \tfrac{1}{2}mc^2.$$

The velocity-distribution has still to be found from the fact that there is a constant total energy, and so it is still of form (46), but with the new value of W. That is

$$f(u, v, w) = \frac{n_0}{(\sqrt{(2\pi)}\sigma)^3} e^{-(mgh + \frac{1}{2}mc^2)/kT}$$

say. Comparing this with (46) itself, $f(u, v, w)$ is seen to be the same as in a uniform gas with the number-density

$$n = n_0 e^{-(mgh)/kT} \qquad . \qquad . \qquad . \qquad (47)$$

Thus the density in the atmosphere considered falls off as the height increases; n_0 gives the number-density at ground level ($h = 0$); at the height $h = kT/mg$, the number-density is n_0/e; at the height $h = 2kT/mg$, it is n_0/e^2; and in general, on rising a distance kT/mg, the density is reduced in the ratio $1/e$.

Another way of seeing what this means is as follows. At any particular level, $f(u, v, w)$ is just the same as in a uniform gas with a suitable n. In such a gas, the effect of collisions can be ignored; collisions bring the gas into the Maxwellian state, but, when once brought into this state, the gas would stay in it even if there were no collisions. Thus the state of the atmosphere, too, is the same as if there were no collisions; the number of molecules at a height h is the number leaving the earth's surface, thinned out because some have insufficient energy to reach the height h. This is the picture given in Chapter VI, when studying forced diffusion.

Again, (46) can be generalized to apply to internal energy. Modern atomic theory asserts that all internal energies are not possible; suppose that the possible internal energies are 0, E_1, E_2, ... Then if a molecule would be just as likely to be in any one energy-state as in any other if an indefinitely large supply of energy were available, the necessity of dividing out a finite ration of energy makes the probabilities that a molecule has internal energies 0, E_1, E_2, ... to be in the ratios

$$1 : e^{-E_1/kT} : e^{-E_2/kT} : \qquad . \qquad . \qquad . \qquad .$$

If E_1, E_2, ... are all large compared with kT, the likelihood that a molecule possesses any internal energy at all becomes very small; this is the result used in Chapter VIII.

Maxwell's is not only the exact velocity-distribution function in the uniform steady state; it is very nearly the correct one in all ordinary gases. Heat conduction and differences of motion and composition do cause slight deviations from Maxwell's law; indeed, viscosity, heat conduction, and the rest are due to such deviations. But the deviations are bound to be very small; they are due to molecules travelling to points where the temperature, etc., are different, and the amount by which the temperature, etc., can alter along a free path is very small. That is why, for example, it is legitimate to use results like

$$\sqrt{(\bar{c}^2)} = 1\cdot086\,\bar{c}$$

in discussing the transport phenomena, even though this result is strictly true only for a gas in a uniform steady state.

CHAPTER XI

THE ATMOSPHERE

Sounding the Atmosphere

THE earth's atmosphere has been studied up to a height of several hundred kilometres above ground level. The properties of the lowest 10 km. or so are well-known from aeroplane ascents; the next few km. have been explored by manned balloons; and yet greater heights have been reached by small balloons carrying self-registering instruments, or instruments whose readings are given by radio signals at definite intervals. By this direct sounding a fairly clear picture has been obtained of the state of the atmosphere up to the highest levels reached (about 30 km.). Still higher levels are just beginning to be explored by rockets like the V2 missiles, but up to now only a little information has been derived by such methods.

In the lowest few km. of the atmosphere, the temperature decreases by nearly 6°C. for every km. risen. At an appropriate height, which varies from place to place, and from time to time in the year, this steady decrease in the temperature suddenly stops, and a layer is reached in which the temperature hardly alters as one ascends further. The lower layer, of decreasing temperature, is called the troposphere; the upper layer, of nearly constant temperature, is the stratosphere; and the surface separating the two layers is known as the tropopause. The height of the tropopause is about 18 km. at the equator, little more than 10 km. in this country, and only about 6 km. at the poles; it is a little greater in summer than in winter. Because of

its greater height at the equator, the lower layers of the stratosphere are actually cooler at the equator (about $-70°$C.) than
at the poles (about $-50°$C.). The lowest few km. of the stratosphere are often accessible to aircraft in this country.

Above the region explored by balloons the air is believed to
get much hotter. Several pieces of evidence pointed to this
even before the direct exploration of such layers by rockets had
begun. The simplest piece of such evidence was the way in
which explosions or heavy gunfire were heard 100 or more
miles away, beyond a zone of silence surrounding the region of
normal audibility. The sound at great distances comes from
above, reflected from the layer of hot air. Sound travels faster
in hot air than in cold, and so, when the upper part of a sound
wave travelling obliquely upward reaches the hot layer it
travels faster than the lower part of the same wave; the wave
front is thus tilted, first forwards and then downwards. The
temperature in the hot zone is believed to be well above that of
the atmosphere near the ground. The hot zone extends 30 km.
or more; above it, the temperature drops to much the same value
as below it.

The region above the hot layer is one which has been
explored by radio. There are several layers in which ultra-
violet light from the sun knocks a large number of electrons
out from their parent molecules, thereby ionizing the latter.
These ionized layers can reflect radio waves which impinge on
them in much the same way as the hot zone below them
reflects sound waves; very long waves are occasionally reflected
at what is called the D-layer, about 65 km. up; medium waves
are reflected at the E-layer, beginning about 100 km. up; and
shorter waves are reflected at the F-layer, 200 or 300 km. up.
The reflected waves tell us a little about the properties of the
layers which reflect them, notably about the number-densities
of molecules in them. The information so obtained indicates
that the temperature above 120 km. may be very high, rising to
a value in the neighbourhood of 1000°C. Densities between
the D and E layers can also be studied by observing the heights
at which meteors are visible.

In the troposphere and the lower stratosphere the amount
of water vapour present falls off very fast with increasing
height; above the lower stratosphere the air is extremely dry.

The clouds make it look as if the upper air is wetter than that near the ground; but this is largely an illusion, due to the fact that the upper air, being cold, cannot hold the little vapour that it has, so that the vapour condenses or freezes out of the air. Wet banks of air do often exist in the atmosphere, but the upper air is frozen dry.

The other chief ingredients of the air—oxygen, nitrogen, and carbon dioxide—are mixed together in almost exactly the same proportions throughout the troposphere, and that part of the stratosphere which has been reached by sounding balloons. There is, however, another minor ingredient of the air which forms a variable proportion of it; this is ozone, itself a form of oxygen, with three atoms to the molecule instead of the usual two. Ozone can be produced by a lightning stroke, and it is also created from more ordinary forms of oxygen by a chemical reaction which goes on about 50 km. up in the atmosphere; it is destroyed when it reaches wet ground, and also by too much sunlight. It usually forms a far larger proportion of the air 25 km. up than near the surface but, like water vapour, it is very variable in amount.

Above the 30 km. level, the atmosphere's composition is less certain. The aurora borealis, or northern lights, originating at heights above 100 km., consists of light of such wavelengths as to make it clear that oxygen and nitrogen are still the chief constituents of the air at these heights. The oxygen is, however, not in the same form as near the ground; the ultra-violet light which knocks electrons out of the molecules to form the E and F layers also knocks the atoms in oxygen molecules apart, and most of the oxygen at great heights consists of separate atoms.

The various hot layers in the upper atmosphere are due to ultra-violet light from the sun. Though nearly transparent to ordinary light, the air has an enormous stopping-power for "ultra" ultra-violet light, which accordingly never reaches the earth. The most extreme ultra-violet light is all stopped by the F-layer; less extreme light is stopped by the E-layer, and moderate ultra-violet light reaches to a height of 40 or 50 km., where it is stopped by the ozone. Any kind of light warms an object on which it falls, just as the sun's visible light warms us when the sun shines brightly; thus the ultra-violet light warms the successive layers which stop and hold it.

K

Any heating of the lower atmosphere happens by a different process. The visible light travels down to the ground, and warms it up; it in turn warms up the air, in part through direct contact, and in part because the earth sends out invisible infrared light (often called radiant heat). Oxygen and nitrogen are as transparent to infra-red light as to the more ordinary visible kind; but water vapour, carbon dioxide and ozone each stop some of the infra-red light from getting away from the earth. The light which they trap warms up the air near the ground; in turn the air keeps the ground warm, like a woolly blanket, or a glasshouse. The analogy with a glasshouse is, indeed, a very apt one; a glasshouse, like the air, keeps warm the air below it by trapping, and sending back, the infra-red light which the earth is continually giving out, and so preventing it from dissipating its energy.

The Scale-height

The pressure p at any level in the atmosphere is just enough to support the weight of the air above that level. The air's weight per unit volume is the density ρ, multiplied by gravity g. Suppose that the actual atmosphere above a given level is replaced by an imaginary atmosphere of the same total weight, but of uniform density equal to the density ρ at that level. Then, to produce the same pressure at that level, this new atmosphere must extend upwards for a height H, where

$$p = \rho g H.$$

The height H is called the homogeneous height, or scale-height, of the atmosphere at the level considered. If n is the number-density of the molecules, and $\bar{m}$ is their mean mass,

$$p = nkT, \quad \rho = n\bar{m}$$

and so

$$H = kT/\bar{m}g. \qquad . \qquad . \qquad . \qquad (48)$$

To see the importance of the scale-height, imagine an atmosphere consisting of a pure gas whose temperature is uniform. The number-density in such an atmosphere was seen in Chapter X to vary with the height h according to the law

$$n = n_0 e^{-mgh/kT} = n_0 e^{-h/H}.$$

Thus the pressure drops in the ratio $1/e$ when h increases by H; that is, the scale-height is the height in which the pressure drops to $1/e$ of its starting value. In the actual atmosphere the temperature varies with height, and so the scale-height also depends on the point chosen; but it is still true that p drops in the ratio $1/e$ on rising a distance equal to the average scale-height in the region considered.

At a temperature of 0°C., with the atmospheric composition

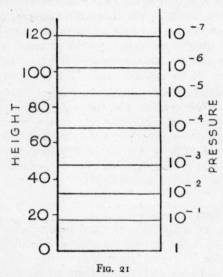

Fig. 21

Heights in the atmosphere at which the pressure is $\frac{1}{10}$, $\frac{1}{100}$, $\frac{1}{1000}$, . . . of that at the ground.

found at the Earth's surface, the scale-height is about 8 km. But it depends both on the temperature and the composition; at the base of the stratosphere it is only three quarters of its ground-level value; in the hot layers above it is much bigger. If at any level the atmosphere were to consist wholly of hydrogen, its scale-height there would be more than seven times as big as that of an atmosphere of the usual composition. Actually there is little reason to believe that hydrogen is an important part of the atmosphere at any level; but at very great heights, where oxygen molecules are largely broken into atoms, the mean mass $\bar{m}$ is an average mass for oxygen atoms and nitrogen molecules, and is appreciably less than lower down. This fact assists the high temperature to raise the scale-height above 120 km. to several times its value at lower levels.

In practice, it is convenient to consider as a scale-height not the height in which the pressure is reduced in the ratio $1/e$, but that in which it is reduced in the ratio $1/10$. The new scale-height is called the decimal scale-height; it is $\log_e 10$, or $2\cdot3$, times the earlier scale-height. Thus it is nearly 20 km. near the earth's surface, about 15 km. in the stratosphere, and perhaps as much as 100 km. in the upper E-layer and the F-layer.

To show diagrammatically how the pressure falls off with height, in Fig. 21 the levels are shown at which the pressure is $\frac{1}{10}, \frac{1}{100}, \frac{1}{1000}, \ldots$ of its ground value. The lower one or two of these levels can be fixed with fair confidence; the positions of the others are less certain. The spacing between two levels is roughly the mean scale-height in the region considered. The large spacing between the third and fourth levels, and between the fourth and fifth, is due to the high temperature in the region above the stratosphere; the hot region above the E-layer is higher than is shown in the figure.

The Mixing Length

Ordinary molecular diffusion and heat conduction are not very important in the air near the ground. The molecules move at high speeds, but they move only a tiny distance before colliding with others, and it takes them a long time to get any appreciable way away from their starting points.

For example, consider the effect of heat conduction. The temperature falls off, on an average, some 6°C. per km. risen; this is the average temperature gradient, but much bigger gradients can arise for short times. Suppose that the temperature gradient is ten times the average, i.e. 6°C. per 10^4 cm. The heat transport due to such a temperature gradient is $\lambda \times 6/10^4$, where λ is the conductivity; also, in the notation of Chapter V,

$$\lambda \times 6/10^4 = \tfrac{1}{2}b\rho lcc \times 6/10^4,$$

where b is, for air, about $1\cdot8$. Suppose this warms a height h of the atmosphere by 1°C. per hour, i.e. per 3600 secs. The air is warmed by constant pressure, and the specific heat at constant pressure is about $1\cdot4c_v$ Thus

$$h\rho \times 1\cdot4c_v \times \tfrac{1}{3600} = 0\cdot9\rho c_v l\bar{c} \times 6/10^4,$$

i.e.

$$h = 1\cdot4l\bar{c}.$$

In this, $\bar{c}$ is about 500 metres, or 5×10^4 cm., per second; l is something like 10^{-5} cm. Hence h is only $0\cdot7$ cm. On the other hand, during a hot summer's day the whole atmosphere up to a height of several hundred metres warms up one or two degrees per hour. Ordinary heat conduction is quite insufficient to explain this heating.

Or again, consider diffusion in the atmosphere. If the atmosphere were allowed to settle down, diffusion would not make it perfectly uniform. Owing to gravity, the heavier molecules would at first diffuse down towards the bottom of the atmosphere; in the steady state which would ultimately be reached, each gas in the atmosphere would fall off with increasing height according to its own scale-height. The scale-height for carbon dioxide is only $\frac{2}{3}$ that for nitrogen; at the height where nitrogen is $\frac{1}{10}$ as plentiful as at the ground, carbon dioxide would be $\left(\frac{1}{10}\right)^{\frac{3}{2}}$, or $\frac{1}{30}$ as plentiful as at the ground. In the actual atmosphere, on the other hand, carbon dioxide falls off practically no faster with increasing height than does nitrogen. The reason is to be found in wind currents, which stir the air up so thoroughly that the heavy molecules are prevented from settling down to the base of the atmosphere.

A theory of the way in which currents stir up the air has been given in terms of a "mixing length" which is very like a free path. Winds are not steady currents, but gusty, irregular, and turbulent; air in them moves from side to side, and up and down, as well as being carried along by them. A rough picture of the motion is to suppose that, in addition to the steady wind flow, masses of air are continually breaking away from their surroundings, travelling some way, and then mixing again into the rest of the atmosphere. They can travel in any direction, though perhaps not equally freely in all directions; their motions between breaking away from their surroundings and being reabsorbed into the rest of the air are very like molecular free paths.

This similarity can be used to derive an "eddy diffusion coefficient". Let $\bar{C}$ be the mean speed of the irregular motions, and L the mean distance which a mass of gas moves while it enjoys a separate existence. The length L, which takes the place of the ordinary free path, is called the mixing length. It is not a very definite length, however, as all the gas is more or less on the move and it is not easy to decide when a mixing length starts or finishes.

For simplicity, neglect variations in the total number-density, but suppose that the number-density n_1 of molecules of a particular ingredient of the air varies with the height. Gas is rising across just half the area of any horizontal plane, and, by analogy with the ordinary theory of diffusion, the mean upward velocity where gas is rising is $\frac{1}{2}\bar{C}$. Hence the number of molecules of the ingredient considered which are carried by rising gas across the plane per second is $\frac{1}{4}n_1\bar{C}$ per unit area of the whole plane. The number carried by descending gas across the plane per second is also $\frac{1}{4}n_1\bar{C}$ per unit area, but with a different n_1. The n_1 for rising gas is that appropriate to a depth L' below the plane, where L' is not very different in size from L; for simplicity, since L is not very exactly defined as yet, let us say that the n_1 is that appropriate to a distance L below the plane. Similarly the n_1 for sinking gas is that appropriate to a height L above the plane; the difference between the two values of n_1 is $2L\gamma$, where γ is the gradient of n_1. The net upward rate of transport of molecules of the special ingredient across the horizontal plane is thus

$$- \tfrac{1}{4}\bar{C} \times 2L\gamma = - \tfrac{1}{2}L\bar{C}\gamma.$$

The corresponding expression for ordinary diffusion was $- D_{12}\,\gamma$; thus eddy motion produces a diffusion coefficient D', where

$$D' = \tfrac{1}{2}L\bar{C}. \qquad \cdot \qquad \cdot \qquad \cdot \qquad (49)$$

This equation is similar in form to that for D_{12}, which was likewise proportional to the mean free path and to the molecular speeds. There is, however, one important difference between eddy diffusion and the molecular variety; eddy motions always mix the atmosphere up thoroughly, while molecular motions tend to bring the heavy molecules into the lower layers.

The mean eddy speed $\bar{C}$ is much smaller than molecular speeds, being rather less than mean wind speeds, i.e. a few metres per second. But whereas the molecular free path is about 10^{-5} cm., the mixing length is usually several metres—many million times as large. Thus it comes about that the eddy diffusion coefficient is far larger than the molecular—often a million times as large; whence follows the smallness of differences of composition in the lower levels of the atmosphere.

Mixing may be less thorough at great heights. Some stirring must undoubtedly occur, for winds do not cease to blow, even when great heights are reached. They seem even to be more vigorous there than lower down: clouds are sometimes seen after sunset, 25 or more km. up, lit by a sun that has left lower levels, moving with the speed of a super-hurricane. But perhaps the winds flow more smoothly there; and in any case the ordinary diffusion coefficient, varying inversely as the pressure, steadily increases with increasing height. Thus at the very top of the atmosphere one would expect to find the different gases separate out to some extent, with the lighter ones on top. In particular, if there is any appreciable amount of hydrogen in the atmosphere one would expect it to diffuse slowly through to the top and, having got there, to stay there.

Convection of Heat

Eddies not only stir up the lower atmosphere; they also affect its temperature. When air rises into a region of less pressure, it expands, and its pressure has to do work in pushing back the air which surrounds it. Since this work has to be provided at the expense of the energy of the molecules, the air must be cooler after rising than before. In the same way, gas which sinks is warmed by the work done in compressing it. The effect of eddies accordingly is to make the atmosphere cooler at great heights, warmer at less. If radiation and molecular conduction of heat are unimportant compared with the effect of eddies, the steady state is one called convective equilibrium. In this, the temperature is 1°C. less for every 100 metres risen; the corresponding temperature gradient amounting to 10°C. per km. is considerably greater than the actual temperature gradient in the troposphere (6°C. per km.).

Eddies convect heat whenever the temperature gradient differs from 10°C. per km.; when the temperature gradient is less, they convect heat down, even though the upper layers are colder than the lower. The upper layers of the troposphere maintain a steady export of heat downward by convection when the temperature is only 6°C. per km.; gas descending arrives at a lower level hotter than that in its new surroundings, while gas rising arrives colder than the air it meets. The export trade from the upper layers is probably supplied chiefly from heat carried up by water vapour; the vapour condenses or freezes as it cools, and gives up to the air its latent heat—the heat originally needed to vaporize it.

The stratosphere has yet another source of heat; ozone in it is able to trap heat rays coming straight from the warm earth, and apparently the warming which results overcomes the effects of convection. Above the stratosphere, convection does not appear to affect the temperature very much.

The "eddy conductivity" of heat can be calculated like the ordinary molecular conductivity, replacing the mean speed $\bar{c}$ of molecules by the mean speed $\bar{C}$ of eddies, and the mean free path l by the mixing length L. Air rising because of eddies cools 10°C. per km. risen; thus it differs in temperature from the level it reaches by $L(\beta - \beta°)$, where β is the actual temperature gradient, and $\beta°$ is one of 10°C. per km. When air mixes into its surroundings, it does so at constant pressure, and so its specific heat must be taken as c_p, that at constant pressure. Hence in place of the molecular conduction of heat $-\lambda\beta$, where

$$\lambda = \tfrac{1}{2}b\rho\bar{l}\bar{c}c_v$$

we get an eddy convection of heat $-\lambda'(\beta - \beta°)$, where

$$\lambda' = \tfrac{1}{2}\rho L\bar{C}c_p. \qquad . \qquad . \qquad (50)$$

The ratio of λ' to λ is roughly the same size as the ratio of the eddy diffusion coefficient to the ordinary one. Since we know that eddies thoroughly mix the troposphere, it is not surprising to find that the eddy conductivity λ' must be very large compared with λ here. Only at very great heights is the ordinary conductivity more important, and here the eddy conductivity is already dominated by ultra-violet light and similar radiations.

An "eddy viscosity" can be calculated like the eddy conductivity and diffusion coefficient. This is μ', where, by analogy with $\mu = \frac{1}{2}a\rho l\bar{c}$ for the molecular viscosity,

$$\mu = \frac{1}{2}\rho\bar{C}L.$$

The L in this is, however, almost certainly smaller than the L in λ'; it is the distance which a mass goes before it loses the horizontal momentum corresponding to the steady wind velocity at the point where it originates, and, because of the way it is buffeted by other masses, it may lose this long before it starts to mix into its surroundings. Indeed, the effects of its continuous buffeting may introduce essential differences between molecular and eddy viscosity; the molecules are pushed about only by collisions, but masses of air are always being pushed about. Nevertheless, though it may be a little doubtful how eddy viscosity acts, it is clear that, like eddy mixing, it is much more important than the molecular kind in the troposphere. And indeed, measurements of the way in which winds increase in speed and change direction in the lowest 2 or 3 km. do indicate an effective viscosity, due to eddies, which may be a million times as large as the molecular. It is an eddy viscosity, likewise, which is responsible for much of the air resistance to fast trains and aircraft.

Escape of the Atmosphere

As we ascend in the atmosphere, the density becomes smaller, and the mean free path of molecules becomes correspondingly larger. At ground level, the free path is something like a hundred-thousandth (10^{-5}) of a centimetre; but in the E-layer, about 120 km. up, it is about a metre; in the F-layer, 250 km. up, it is about 30 metres. At greater heights, yet longer free paths are met; at last, near the very top of the atmosphere—say at heights above 1000 km.—free paths are very long, and collisions are rare accidents.

At such heights molecules describe long paths under gravity, undisturbed by each other. Like a rocket, each molecule shoots up from below, curves over, and plunges back into the denser gas below; it is shot up from a collision in the denser gas, and its later fall is unchecked until it again suffers a collision. The top layer, in which very few collisions can take place, contains only about as many molecules as a layer one free path thick at the ground; these would occupy only 10^{-5} cm. at the ground, but are spread through many km. in the top layer. There may be, say, 50 million molecules per cubic cm. where this top layer begins; this sounds fairly large but it is intensely small compared with the number of ground level. As the Red Queen might have remarked to Alice, "Talking of atmospheres, I have seen atmospheres compared with which this is a vacuum."

If a molecule were shot up into this top layer with too great a speed, it could escape completely from the Earth's gravitational pull, and go wandering off into space. The least speed which would enable it to escape would be $\sqrt{(2ga)}$, where a is its distance from the Earth's centre when it starts, and g is the acceleration due to the Earth's pull at this distance. Taking the starting height to be 1000 km. from the Earth's surface, this gives a least speed of escape equal to about 10 km. per second. Even at a temperature of 1000°C., the mean velocity of hydrogen molecules is only 3·7 km. per second, and that of oxygen and nitrogen molecules only about 1 km. per second; the mean speed would be less at a lower temperature. Collisions give only a small fraction of the molecules a speed much in excess of the mean speed; nevertheless, molecules will occasionally be shot right clear of the earth's influence.

The number of molecules escaping can be estimated very crudely as follows. A molecule is able to escape simply because the Earth's gravity fades out as the molecule gets further away. If gravity were the same at all heights, no molecules whatsoever could escape; molecules with an upward speed greater than $\sqrt{(2ga)}$ would rise a distance at least equal to a, but would then fall back. Thus in this case the number given an upward speed at least equal to $\sqrt{(2ga)}$ per second would be the total number travelling up per second at a height a above the starting level; this is $\frac{1}{4}n\bar{c}$ per unit area, where $\bar{c}$ is the mean speed and n the number-density at the height reached. Now n would be $n_0 e^{-a/H}$, where n_0 is the number-density at the starting level, and H the scale-height; $\bar{c}$ is presumably much the same as the mean velocity at the starting level. Hence the number of molecules per second rising across the starting level with upward speeds at least equal to $\sqrt{(2ga)}$ would be $\frac{1}{4} n_0 \bar{c} e^{-a/H}$. This would be the result if, as we have said, gravity did not fade out as the height increases; but the number of molecules with any special speed at the starting level can hardly depend on the state of the gas above, and so the expression $\frac{1}{4} n_0 \bar{c} e^{-a/H}$ must be correct even when gravity does vary with the height.

However, this expression only gives the molecules with an *upward* speed greater than $\sqrt{(2ga)}$; actually all molecules travelling upward which have a total speed greater than $\sqrt{(2ga)}$ are able to escape, at least if they are not moving so nearly horizontally that they have to travel a very long way in relatively dense air at the start, and so are likely to be stopped by a collision. The total number escaping is therefore more than $\frac{1}{4} n_0 \bar{c} e^{-a/H}$; it is, in fact,

$$\frac{1}{4} n_0 \bar{c} \left(1 + \frac{a}{H} \right) e^{-a/H} \quad . \quad . \quad . \quad (52)$$

The factor a/H is actually fairly large; $2ga$ is the square of the escape speed, while $2gh$ is $\pi/4$ times the square of a molecule's mean speed. But the important factor in the expression (52) is not $1 + a/H$, but $e^{-a/H}$, which is usually very tiny.

For example, suppose that the top of the atmosphere consists wholly of nitrogen at 1000°C.; then $\bar{c}$ is about 1 km. per second, and $/H$ is about 125. Hence $e^{-a/H}$ is about 10^{-54}, and, taking $n_0 = 50$ million, the number of nitrogen molecules escaping per second is only 10^{-40} per square centimetre of the earth's surface. A loss so tiny as this would be perfectly inappreciable, even in the 3000 million years that the Earth is believed to have existed.

For hydrogen, the result would be very different. If there were an appreciable amount of hydrogen in the atmosphere, this would tend to rise to the top, and, because the scale-height is so much bigger for hydrogen than for other gases, in the upper part of the atmosphere it would become the most plentiful gas present. If the top of the atmosphere was hydrogen at 1000°C., $\bar{c}$ would be 3·7 km. per second, and a/H would be only 9. Hence $e^{-a/H}$ would be $10^{-3\cdot9}$, and, again taking $n_0 = 50$

million, the number of hydrogen molecules escaping per second is 5000 million per square cm. of the Earth's surface.

The escape in this case would be quite fast. The hydrogen in the Earth's atmosphere can hardly constitute more than 0·01 per cent of all the molecules present, judging by surface measurements, and the total number of molecules would extend to the scale-height of 8 km. if packed uniformly at the surface number-density (2·7 × 10^{18} per cubic cm.). There are thus at most 2·2 × 10^{21} hydrogen molecules above a square cm. of the Earth; if these are being lost at a rate of 5000 million per second, they will last only 4·4 × 10^{11} seconds, or 14,000 years.

Clearly, therefore, hydrogen would be lost from the top of the atmosphere far too fast for a permanent hydrogen layer to exist there. Any hydrogen in the atmosphere must stay in it for only a short while; it presumably comes by the decomposition of gases like marsh gas, and either escapes, or combines with oxygen to form water, before any appreciable quantity of it can collect at the top of the atmosphere. Helium, like hydrogen, is likely to escape rapidly if the temperature of the upper atmosphere is 1000°C., though the time it would take to escape would be millions, not thousands, of years. But no other gas in the atmosphere is likely to escape to any appreciable extent.

The rate of escape is smaller for heavy gases than for light, because it depends on the scale-height, or, what is equivalent, on the mean molecular velocity, which is less for heavy gases than light. For the same reason, the rate of escape depends on the temperature; if the top of the atmosphere were as cool as the air near the ground, even hydrogen would be unable to escape, but if it were hotter than 1000°C. many other gases might escape. The earth is believed to have been formed from the sun; but whereas hydrogen is comfortably the most plentiful element in the sun, and iron is very rare in it, the reverse is true in the Earth. It is believed that, during the early stages of the Earth's formation, while it was still very hot, it lost most of its hydrogen, shooting it off into outer space.

Of course, the rate of escape also depends on the strength of gravitation. A lighter body than the Earth, exerting less gravitational pull, would find it hard to retain any atmosphere;

in fact, the moon has none. On the other hand, large planets like Jupiter (300 times as massive as the Earth) or Saturn (100 times) could probably retain even their hydrogen, assuming that it was not dissipated when they were first formed. They are much less dense than the Earth, and this may be due to their consisting in large part of light gases (perhaps in a frozen form).

The Earth is not only losing gas from the top of its atmosphere; a reverse process also goes on. Everyone knows that meteors are continually shooting into the upper atmosphere, and burning themselves out as "shooting stars". But, apart from this, the Earth is also picking up matter in a much less spectacular way. The space round the Earth is not quite empty; it is full of extremely rare gas, some shot out from the sun, and some coming from elsewhere. The Earth is continually sweeping up such gas—plucking it from neighbouring space by its gravitational pull. On the balance it is quite likely to be gaining more than it loses.

CHAPTER XII

ELECTRICITY IN GASES

Ions and Electrons

ELECTRICITY is able to move through gases simply because some of the molecules are ionized, and so carry electric charges. In normal circumstances not many of them are ionized, and so a gas is a good insulator. But electricity does leak very slowly through a gas, showing that a few ions are always present to carry it about.

There are many ways in which ions can be produced. Sometimes an electron is knocked off one molecule when another molecule collides with it. This happens very rarely in ordinary gases at ordinary temperatures; an electron is not detached unless a fairly violent collision takes place, and at ordinary temperatures molecular energies are insufficient to provide sufficiently violent collisions. But in the heat of a flame, molecules move much faster, and many electrons are broken away from their molecules. The ions which they leave behind, being incomplete molecules, are always ready to pick up new electrons when occasion offers, and so, when gas leaves a flame, most molecules do not remain charged for long; but the last few ions have to hunt for a long time to find an electron, and so the last traces of ionization may persist for a long while. Near an industrial city, where factory and domestic chimneys both emit plenty of smoke, ions can be detected some miles downwind.

Other ions are produced by radiation. Near the top of the atmosphere, as we have seen, the sun's ultra-violet light knocks electrons off the molecules to create the E and F ionized layers. In a laboratory, X-rays can be used in much the same way to ionize molecules; but whereas ultra-violet light only succeeds in detaching one of the outermost electrons from a molecule, X-rays are perfectly capable of knocking an electron out of its innermost parts.

Again, most surface rocks contain a very tiny amount of radioactive material; as this decays, it sends out very penetrating radiation and fast charged particles, both of which can knock electrons out of the air molecules which they meet. In fact, many of the ions in the lowest km. or two of the atmosphere are due to radioactivity. Above this lowest km. or two, a more important source of ions is the so-called cosmic rays—very fast particles coming down from above, and again ionizing molecules by collision. Ionization by radioactivity and cosmic rays ensures that an odd ion or two is always likely to be present in an ordinary gas.

Mobilities

Suppose that gas is between two parallel metal plates maintained at different voltages, so that an electric field, of intensity X, say, acts between the plates. Then an ion carrying an electric charge e is acted on by a force eX, which makes it diffuse through the rest of the gas. The speed of ions due to this force was found in Chapter VI to be

$$u = D_{12}eX/kT$$

where D_{12} is the coefficient of diffusion of ions through the rest of the gas. It is customary to write

$$u = KX$$

where K is called the *mobility* of the ions. Thus

$$K = e\, D_{12}/kT \qquad . \qquad . \qquad . \qquad (53)$$

Since D_{12} is inversely proportional to the pressure p, the same should be true of K for any particular kind of ion. Experiments do, in fact, confirm that u/X is proportional to $1/p$ for ordinary values of p and X.

The original experimenters on ion mobility were at first not clear as to the nature of the charged particles in a gas. They lumped together all positively charged particles as positive ions, and all negatively charged particles as negative ions, and found that negative ions had a rather greater mobility than positive, but that mobilities seemed to depend greatly on the conditions. Mobilities in damp air, for example, were much less than those in dry air; and newly created ions were often far more mobile than the same ions after existing some time. After a while it came to be recognized that many sorts of ion, both positive and negative, are usually present in a gas, and that different types of ion predominate in different conditions. The simplest negative ions are electrons, which, because of their small masses and high speeds, have great mobilities. However, several kinds of molecule, like oxygen and water vapour, are always ready to pick up a free electron when they meet it. Thus few free electrons are to be found in any ordinary ionized gas; even so, those few materially increase the average mobility of negative ions as a whole.

An ion possesses an electric charge because it has an electron too many or too few. Thus, when the charge of an electron had once been measured, the coefficient of diffusion D_{12} could be determined from the mobility K. The coefficient of diffusion was found to be usually much less than that for ordinary gases, implying that the ions were either bigger than uncharged molecules, or heavier, or both.

There is actually no reason why an ion should not be bigger than an uncharged molecule. The size of the ion is fixed by the distance at which it begins to push or pull other molecules about, and, because of its charge, it begins to pull at the electrons on other molecules when still some way off. But the large apparent size due to such electric forces is not the only reason for the smallness of D_{12}. Some kinds of molecule, especially those of water vapour, tend to form clusters round an electric charge, and the ion consists often of a cluster of six or more molecules. Such a cluster moves like a massive super-molecule, sluggishly, and its slow motions are reflected in the smallness of D_{12}.

If the apparent size of an ion is due solely to the way in which its electric charge pulls at the electrons on other molecules, the size should not depend on the particular kind of ion which carries the electric charge, though it may depend on the nature of the molecules through which it moves. That is, in the formula for D_{12}, given in Chapter VI as

$$D_{12} = \frac{0.6 \sqrt{(\bar{c}_1{}^2 + \bar{c}_2{}^2)}}{2\pi (r_1 + r_2)^2 (n_1 + n_2)}$$

the sum of the radii, $r_1 + r_2$, is independent of the particular kind of ion. Hence if several different kinds if ion move in turn through the same gas, their coefficients of diffusion D_{12}, and mobilities K, should be proportional to the corresponding values of $\sqrt{(\bar{c}_1{}^2 + \bar{c}_2{}^2)}$, i.e. of

$$\sqrt{\left(\frac{1}{m_1} + \frac{1}{m_2}\right)} = \sqrt{\left(\frac{m_1 + m_2}{m_1 m_2}\right)}$$

Thus, if m_1 refers to the ions, m_2 to the gas through which they move,

$$K \propto \sqrt{\left(1 + \frac{m_2}{m_1}\right)}$$

for the different kinds of ion.

Tyndall and his co-workers have recently found mobilities for several kinds of positive ion in nitrogen. The ions are chiefly positively charged molecules of metals, but, so far as mobilities are concerned, they can be treated like gas molecules. The experiments were so conducted that clustering round an ion could be ignored. The experimental results are shown in Fig. 22, a curve $K \propto \sqrt{(1 + m_2/m_1)}$ being also shown for comparison. The experimental results lie very nearly on this curve, save for nitrogen ions, whose mobility in nitrogen is low. Atomic theory explains the discrepancy for nitrogen ions by the fact that an electron can pass from a nitrogen molecule to a nitrogen ion without any energy having to be supplied or disposed of; this makes a nitrogen molecule to be more seriously

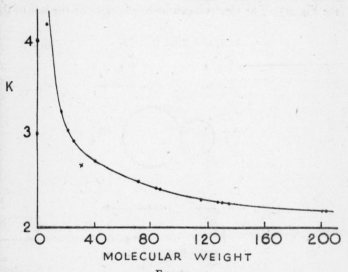

FIG. 22

Mobility K of several kinds of positive ion in nitrogen, plotted against the molecular weight of the ions. Ions other than those of nitrogen are shown by dots, nitrogen ions by a cross. The continuous curve is a curve $K \propto \sqrt{(1 + m_2/m_1)}$ where m_1 refers to ions, m_2 to nitrogen.

affected by a nitrogen ion near it than by a different ion, and so increases the apparent size of the nitrogen ion.

Electron-temperatures

When electrons move in a strong electric field, there need not be equipartition of energy between them and the gas molecules through which they move. During a free path, their speeds are increased appreciably by the electric field, and the smallness of their mass makes it very difficult for them to get

L

rid of their extra energy when they collide with the gas molecules.

Consider, for example, what happens in a "direct" collision,
when an electron collides with a molecule which is travelling
along the same line. Call the masses of the electron and the
molecule m_1 and m_2; suppose that before colliding the speeds
of the two are c_1 and c_2, and after colliding they are c'_1 and c'_2
(see Fig. 23). The electron can be to the right or the left of the

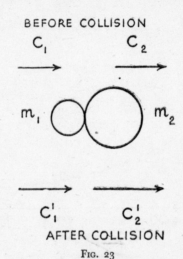

BEFORE COLLISION

AFTER COLLISION

Fig. 23

Velocities of an electron and a molecule
before and after a direct collision.

molecule; also each of c_1, c_2, c'_1, c'_2 can be positive (to the right)
or negative (to the left). The total momentum and energy are
the same before and after the collision; thus

$$m_1 c_1 + m_2 c_2 = m_1 c'_1 + m_2 c'_2,$$
$$\tfrac{1}{2} m_1 c_1{}^2 + \tfrac{1}{2} m_2 c_2{}^2 = \tfrac{1}{2} m_1 c'_1{}^2 + \tfrac{1}{2} m_2 c'_2{}^2.$$

These equations can be rewritten as

$$m_1 (c_1 - c'_1) = m_2 (c'_2 - c_2),$$
$$\tfrac{1}{2} m_1 (c_1{}^2 - c'_1{}^2) = \tfrac{1}{2} m_2 (c'_2{}^2 - c_2{}^2).$$

Dividing the second of these equations by the first,

$$c_1 + c'_1 = c'_2 + c_2,$$

or

$$c_1 - c_2 = c'_2 - c'_1.$$

That is, the relative velocity of the electron and the molecule has the same size before and after the collision. But, because of their lightness, electrons move much faster than molecules, and so the relative velocity is nearly all due to the speed of the electron. Thus the speed of an electron and its energy are hardly altered by a collision.

Similar results apply when the electron and the molecule are travelling along different lines before colliding. In this case the relative velocity is altered in direction by the collision, but its size is again unaltered. Roughly speaking, collisions hardly alter electrons' energies, but they change their directions of motion in a more or less random fashion. In consequence, in a fairly strong electric field electrons acquire greater energies than the molecules, but have little preference for one direction of motion above another. A "temperature" T_1 of the electrons can be defined as such that the mean energy E_1 of electrons is equal to $\frac{3}{2} kT_1$. The temperature of the gas as a whole is chiefly determined by the mean energy E_2 of the molecules, which are much more plentiful than the electrons; the electron temperature is thus much greater than that of the gas as a whole.

To estimate E_1, the average small loss in energy of an electron at a collision must be balanced against the average small gain in energy during a free path, due to the action of the electric field. Consider direct collisions again. The electron's loss of energy at a collision is

$$\tfrac{1}{2}m_1 c_1{}^2 - \tfrac{1}{2}m_1 c'_1{}^2 = \tfrac{1}{2}m_1 (c_1 - c'_1)(c_1 + c'_1).$$

Again

$$(m_1 + m_2) c'_1 = m_1 c'_1 + m_2 c'_2 - m_2 (c'_2 - c'_1)$$
$$= m_1 c_1 + m_2 c_2 - m_2 (c_1 - c_2).$$

Using the value of c'_1 given by this equation, the loss in energy becomes

$$\frac{2\,m_1\,m_2}{(m_1 + m_2)^2}\,(c_1 - c_2)\,(m_1\,c_1 + m_2\,c_2).$$

The average value of this depends on the mean values of $c_1{}^2$, $c_1\,c_2$, and $c_2{}^2$. If the electron and molecule were just two taken at random, the mean value of c_2 would be zero—the molecule can move backward or forward—and so the mean value of $c_1 c_2$ would also vanish. Also the mean values of $m_1 c_1{}^2$ and $m_2 c_2{}^2$ would be $2E_1$ and $2E_2$; thus the average loss in energy would be

$$\frac{4\,m_1\,m_2}{(m_1 + m_2)^2}\,(E_1 - E_2) \quad . \quad . \quad . \quad (54)$$

However, the electron and the molecule are not just two taken at random; an electron tends to collide with a molecule coming in the opposite direction rather than with one travelling in the same direction, and fast electrons collide more often than slow. The effect is that the average loss in energy is rather different from (54)—the numerical factor should not be 4, but something rather less. The numerical factor is also somewhat less when collisions other than direct ones are considered; the mean loss, averaged over all collisions, can be shown to be only about one-third of that given by (54). For electrons in air, m_2 is more than 50,000 times as large as m_1; thus an electron loses, on an average, only about one forty-thousandth part of its excess energy when it collides with a molecule.

Immediately after colliding with a molecule, an electron is just as likely to be moving in one direction as in another. If electrons travelled with unaltered velocities during their free paths the electric field would do no work on them, on an average. However, during a free path, an electron has an acceleration eX/m_1, where e is its charge. During the time τ taken by the free path, this acceleration makes it move a distance $\tfrac{1}{2}\tau^2 eX/m_1$ parallel to the electric field, and, as a result, the force eX acting on it increases its energy by $\tfrac{1}{2}\tau^2 e^2 X^2/m_1$. The mean value of this, averaged over all free paths, equals the mean loss of energy at a collision, about one-third of (54). Hence

$$\tfrac{1}{2}\overline{\tau^2}e^2X^2/m_1 = \tfrac{4}{3}\frac{m_1 m_2}{(m_1 + m_2)^2}(E_1 - E_2),$$

or, remembering that m_1/m_2 is very small, roughly

$$E_1 - E_2 = \tfrac{3}{8}m_2\overline{\tau^2}e^2X^2/m_1^2.$$

This equation does not immediately fix E_1, since $\overline{\tau^2}$ itself depends on E_1; the average time taken by an electron to

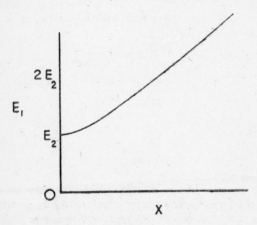

$2E_2$

E_1

E_2

O

X

Fig. 24

Graph of electron-energy E_1 against field X.

travel the free path between two successive collisions with molecules is $l/\overline{c_1}$, where l is the mean free path. Very roughly, we can put

$$\overline{\tau^2} = l^2/\overline{c_1^2} = \tfrac{1}{2}m_1 l^2/E_1$$

and so, equally roughly,

$$E_1(E_1 - E_2) = \tfrac{3}{16}m_2 l^2 e^2 X^2/m_1 . \qquad . \quad (55)$$

If l is independent of the electron-temperature, this makes E_1 roughly proportional to X when X is fairly large, the variation of E_1 with X being that indicated in Fig. 24. However, in practice l does depend somewhat on the electron-temperature, the apparent size of a molecule varying in a rather peculiar fashion when electrons of different speeds are fired at it.

The mobility K of electrons tends to be reduced by an increase in the electron-temperature. The rate of their diffusion in an electric field depends on the amount by which the field can alter their velocity in a free path, and so is proportional to the time taken by a free path. The formula for K now is

$$K = \frac{eD_{12}}{kT_1}$$

and, since n_2 is large compared with n_1, and $\bar{c_1}$ is large compared with $\bar{c_2}$, roughly

$$D_{12} = 0 \cdot 3 \bar{c_1} l.$$

Thus

$$K = \frac{0 \cdot 3 e \bar{c_1} l}{\frac{1}{3} m_1 \bar{c_1}^2},$$

or roughly

$$K = \frac{e\tau}{m_1}$$

When X is very large, formulae like (55) cease to apply. In deriving the formula, any energy given up by an electron when it collides with a molecule was supposed to increase the energy of translation of the molecule; it was not supposed to set the molecule rotating or vibrating. Actually an electron has too little mass to set the molecule as a whole rotating, or to make one whole atom in the molecule vibrate relative to the rest; but it may alter the motion of electrons in the molecule. A certain minimum energy is required to lift an electron in the molecule from its usual path into another of its permitted paths, and this energy is far more than is possessed by a molecule in normal circumstances.

In a strong electric field, however, free electrons may acquire more than this minimum energy; when they do, they may be able, when colliding with a molecule, to knock an electron in the molecule into a different permitted path. In this case, most of the energy of the colliding electron is transferred to the electron inside the molecule, and energy of translation disappears; the collision is said to be "inelastic". After an inelastic collision, the electron inside the molecule returns to its starting position, either by transforming the energy which it has just received into kinetic energy of translation when another particle collides with the molecule (a "hyperelastic" collision, in which the colliding particles spring apart faster than they came together) or by converting this energy into light. If much energy is turned into light the gas starts to glow. Very fast free electrons may not simply disturb the electrons in a molecule with which they collide; they may knock them clear of the molecule and ionize it. When many electrons are knocked clear in this fashion a noisy electrical discharge may result.

Discharges

An electrical discharge originally meant simply a process whereby a body possessing an electric charge lost this charge more or less rapidly; but it has now come to mean any process in which electricity passes fairly rapidly through a gas. Several different sorts of discharge are possible. One is a quiet, steady discharge in a rarefied gas; this is the sort which occurs in an X-ray tube, or in the neon tubes used for advertising, or in the new fluorescent lighting. Another is the noisy, crackling spark which may occur at ordinary pressure; the lightning is the most striking example of this. A third is the glow discharge that sometimes takes place at an electrified metal point; this is noticed at the tip of a lightning conductor during a thunderstorm, or on parts of an aeroplane flying through a thundercloud. There are many others.

Quiet discharges are distinguished from sudden outbursts by the way in which electrons are produced. In a low-pressure discharge there is a steady flow of electrons one way and of positive ions the other way. The positive ions are drawn into the cathode (the negatively charged plate) with sufficient speeds to knock out the electrons needed to keep the discharge going. The electrons acquire considerable energy as they travel down the tube; part of this is used in enabling the molecules to emit light, part in knocking other electrons out of molecules and so producing the positive ions also needed to keep the discharge going. The discharge is steady because it continuously supplies enough charged particles to make up for those drawn up to the terminal plates, and there lost.

A spark discharge, however, depends far more on accidents. Many of the individual features of a spark are still obscure, but a theory advanced in the last few years by Loeb and Meek seems to explain most of its essential features. This theory asserts that a spark is set going by a single electron, if all the circumstances are favourable. In one cubic centimetre of atmospheric air, some 10 or so molecules are ionized per second by cosmic rays and terrestrial radioactivity.

Suppose that two plates are maintained at a potential difference of some thousands of volts, and suppose that an electron is produced near the cathode by radioactivity, cosmic rays, or some other agency. The electric field drives it towards the anode (positive plate); after a few free paths it has acquired enough kinetic energy to ionize another molecule. After this there are two free electrons; these, again, travel for a few free paths and then are able to ionize further molecules.

The process goes on cumulatively; by the time they reach the anode there may be millions of electrons. They move across the gap between the plates with a speed much less than the random speeds with which they travel along their free paths; nevertheless, because the free-path movements are random—sometimes back, sometimes forward—while they drift steadily across the gap, they do not separate very far as they move across. The group of travelling electrons can fitly be called an electron avalanche. The avalanche leaves behind a number of positive ions which, travelling relatively sluggishly, are still more or less in the places where they were created when the avalanche plunges into the anode. They fill a sort of tubular region between the anode and the cathode (see Fig. 25).

Many of the avalanches are relatively tame affairs and lead to no striking results. This is especially true of the avalanches that travel only short distances. If an avalanche consists of, say, a million electrons after travelling one centimetre, it consists of only a thousand after travelling the first half centimetre; each of these produces a thousand more in travelling the other half centimetre. An avalanche which had only half a centimetre to travel before plunging into the anode would be very weak in comparison with that travelling one centimetre. After such a weak avalanche, the positive ions leak slowly away to the cathode and there surrender their charges, and nothing permanent results. Even a strong avalanche is not itself an electric spark; but when it attains its greatest strength, just before it plunges into the anode, it may be able to initiate other processes which lead to the spark.

Before the true spark, a "streamer" has to be formed. Only a small part of the kinetic energy which avalanche electrons

CATHODE

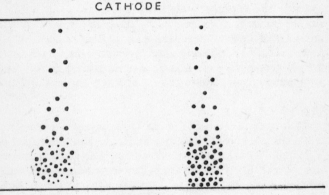

ANODE

FIG. 25

Stages in the development of an electric spark. On the left, an avalanche about to reach the anode; on the right, a streamer beginning to travel back from the anode to the cathode. Positive ions are shown by large dots, electrons by small.

derive from the electric field is used in ionizing molecules; much more is used in enabling the molecules to give out light. The light given out may, in some cases, ionize other molecules some way from the original avalanche, and so produce electrons which start further avalanches. If the original avalanche is a strong one, it leaves behind it a large number of positive charges; these may be enough to attract the electrons of some of the new avalanches into their tube, especially near its "head" (near the anode) where the positive ions are most numerous.

The light produced by the new avalanches ionizes other

M

molecules behind the head of the tube, and so produces further avalanches which strengthen the head of the tube and extend it backward (see Fig. 25). The backward extension, being due to light, travels much faster than even an electron would; its speed is actually about ten times that of the original avalanche The extension travels back across the gap, increasing in strength as it goes; the extension brings the "streamer" into being. When the streamer has travelled a good way across the gap, its light, and the electric field which it produces, begin to draw further electrons from the cathode. At last these join up with the streamer; electrons begin to pour out of the cathode in large numbers, many more are produced by avalanches and light in the streamer, and the whole streamer becomes full of electrons and positive ions, carrying their charges across the gap. A large electric current is then able to travel across from plate to plate, and this is the true spark.

Metals

It may appear altogether incongruous to consider metals in a book on gases. However, as Drude first suggested forty years ago, electrons in a metal constitute something like a gas. Most of the electrons are bound to their parent molecules in the usual way; but certain of them—usually one per molecule— are shared between the molecules and can move more or less freely among them, though not able, in normal circumstances, to escape from the metal as a whole.

Many of the observed properties of metals can be explained by assuming the existence of this sort of "electron-gas." Because of their great speeds, electrons can transport energy very efficiently from point to point; this explains why metals are good conductors of heat. Again, metals are also good conductors of electricity, because so many electrons are present ready to be set diffusing past the molecules when an electric field acts on them. Moreover, if in a circuit composed of two wires the junctions are maintained at different temperatures, an electric current flows round the circuit; this is due to a "thermal diffusion" of the electrons, different in strength in the two wires. Finally, if a wire is heated, the faster electrons get enough energy to be able to escape from the forces by which the molecules seek to retain them, and leak into outer space, much as molecules jump out of a liquid as it evaporates; this fact underlies the construction of all radio valves.

If the heat conductivity λ is due to motions of the electrons, arguments like those of Chapter V show that

$$\lambda = \tfrac{1}{2} b \rho l \bar{c} c_v,$$

where $\bar{c}$ is the mean speed of electrons, c_v their specific heat, ρ their density, and l their mean free path between successive collisions with atoms; b is a pure number comparable with unity. If electrons form a gas like an ordinary gas, their specific heat is $\tfrac{3}{2} k/m$, where m is the electronic mass; also if n is the number-density of electrons, $\rho = mn$. Thus

$$\lambda = \tfrac{3}{4} bnklc. \quad . \qquad . \qquad . \qquad . \quad (56)$$

The electrical conductivity σ is defined as such that a current σX flows when an electric field X acts along a wire of cross-section one square cm. Now, if the field X makes the electrons diffuse through the atoms with speed u, the number crossing one square cm. in a second is nu; the current produced is the charge carried across the square cm. by these electrons, i.e., neu, where e is the electronic charge. Thus

$$\sigma X = neu = ne\,KX,$$

where K is the electron-mobility. Again

$$K = \frac{e}{kT} D_{12}$$

where D_{12} is the coefficient of diffusion of electrons through the atoms. This has to be calculated rather differently from the coefficient of diffusion in Chapter VI, where pressure changes were supposed to push the gas about; here the molecules are immovable. By an argument like that giving equation (25) in Chapter VI,

$$D_{12} = \tfrac{1}{2} dl\bar{c}$$

where d is another pure number. Hence, finally,

$$\sigma = ne\,K = \frac{ne^2}{kT} D_{12} = \frac{ne^2}{2kT} dl\bar{c}. \quad . \qquad . \quad (57)$$

Equations (56) and (57) can be combined to give

$$\frac{\lambda}{\sigma} = \frac{2}{3}\frac{b}{d}\left(\frac{k}{e}\right)^2 T \qquad . \qquad . \qquad . \qquad (58)$$

Thus, at a given temperature, λ/σ should be the same for all metals. This is the law of Wiedemann and Franz, found experimentally in 1853; it is roughly true for pure metals at ordinary temperatures, though alloys give rather different values of λ/σ. For any special metal, (58) indicates that λ/σ should be proportional to T; this is roughly true at ordinary temperatures, but not at low.

To this extent, then, Drude's theory gave quantitative agreement with experiment; but it was soon recognized as subject to difficulties. For example, the free path of an electron should be about the same size as the average distance between neighbouring metal atoms, since these appear to be jammed more or less tightly together; the free path calculated from (57), using experimental values of σ, is several times as large as this, even at ordinary temperatures. At very low temperatures the difficulty is far greater; a current started in metal immersed in liquid helium does not die away for hours, indicating an enormous conductivity, and free paths many kilometres long.

Again, if electrons form a gas in the metal, they should contribute to its specific heat. The atoms must be free to vibrate to and fro in the metal; the principle of equipartition of energy indicates that the part of the vibration of an atom parallel to Ox, Oy, or Oz must have mean kinetic energy $\frac{1}{2}kT$ and an equal mean potential energy, so that the mean total energy of the atom is $3kT$. The mean energy of an electron should be $\frac{3}{2}kT$; thus, if there is one free electron per atom, the total energy of the metal is $\frac{9}{2}kT$ per atom. However, specific heats suggest a total energy only $3kT$ per atom at ordinary temperatures. That is, either the electrons are much fewer than one per atom—which would only aggravate the free-path difficulty—or they, for some reason, do not contribute to the specific heat. The second alternative did not, for a long time, seem credible. Experiments showed that electrons given out by a hot wire have, at least very nearly, a Maxwellian velocity-distribution function; this suggested that electrons in the metal have the same velocity-distribution, and form an ordinary gas.

The quantum theory was, however, able to resolve the difficulty. It asserted that electrons shared among the metal molecules, like those bound, are free to move only in certain paths, and to possess only certain definite energies. So many electrons are present that all the possible paths of small energy are occupied by electrons, and the only empty paths are paths of high energy. The electron velocity-distribution function is

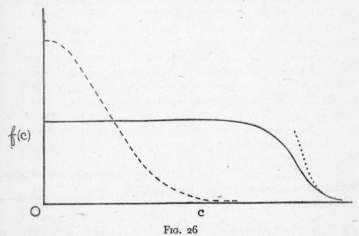

FIG. 26

Electron velocity-distribution function in a metal (continuous curve) and Maxwell's velocity-distribution function (broken curve). The dotted curve on the right, joining on to the continuous curve, is Maxwell's function on a greatly magnified vertical scale.

not Maxwell's, but a different function $f(c)$ of the molecular speed c.

This function is illustrated in Fig. 26, where Maxwell's function is shown for comparison. The straight part of the curve in this figure corresponds to small energies, where all available electron-paths are full; the "tail" on the right, corresponding to energies where only a few of the possible paths are occupied, is much the same as the corresponding part of Maxwell's curve, though on a very different scale. This explains why electrons "evaporating" from a hot metal have a nearly Maxwellian velocity-distribution; for it is only the high-energy electrons which manage to escape.

As Fig. 26 illustrates, the electrons have a higher mean kinetic energy than they would have if their velocity-distribution were Maxwellian; they are forced to occupy states of higher energy than they would otherwise do, because the possible states of lower energy are all occupied. But their high energies do not mean that their specific heat is high. Consider what happens when the temperature drops. The electrons corresponding to the flat part of Fig. 26 cannot lose energy, for all the possible paths of less energy are already full. Only the few electrons corresponding to the "tail" in Fig. 26 can lose energy; when they do, the flat part of the curve extends a little further to the right, and the "tail" corresponds to rather fewer electrons. Because the change in temperature affects only the few electrons corresponding to the "tail", the specific heat of the electrons is small. At ordinary temperatures it is, in fact, only one or two per cent of the specific heat which the electrons would have if they formed an ordinary gas; the mean speed of the electrons on the other hand, is, say, ten times that given by the ordinary gas formulae.

This implies changes in the formulae for λ and σ. The heat conduction is still given by a formula of the form

$$\lambda = \tfrac{1}{2} b \rho l c \bar{c}_v$$

but with altered values of $\bar{c}$ and c_v. The electrical conductivity is given by a formula like (57), but with T replaced by the electron temperature T', defined as such that $\tfrac{3}{2} k T'$ is the mean kinetic energy of an electron. Formula (58), strangely enough, remains unaltered in form, save for a slight change in the numerical constant—a useful fact, for this formula was the one whose agreement with experiment was originally held to justify Drude's theory of metals.

The electrical conductivity, like the electron mobility earlier, is proportional to $l/\bar{c}$, the mean time taken by a free path, since the conductivity is due to the motion which the electric field gives electrons during a free path. We have just seen that $\bar{c}$ is ten times that given by ordinary gas formulae at ordinary temperatures; to balance this, l must also be increased tenfold, to explain observed values of σ. The free path required at ordinary temperatures to explain the conductivity of actual metals is, in fact, something like a hundred times the distance between neighbouring atoms—this in spite of the fact that the atoms are packed so tightly that, if they were solid, they would be nearly in contact.

The quantum theory explains this difficulty by showing that the permitted paths of electrons are such that they can move without let or hindrance through the gaps between the atoms, provided only that the atoms are arranged perfectly regularly in order, like soldiers on parade. In a pure metal the atoms are, in fact, arranged in perfect order at low temperatures, whence the enormous electrical conductivity of metals at such temperatures. As the temperature rises, however, the atoms start to vibrate to and fro with steadily increasing violence; the resulting irregularity of their order enables them somewhat to check the free passage of electrons through them, though the free path still remains large. Impurities in a metal, by breaking up the regular order of the atoms, likewise obstruct the passage of electrons.

Electrons in a metal can, therefore, only by courtesy be said to form a gas. In a gas, the molecules are widely separated, and their free paths are paths in which they are unaffected by others. But the free path of an electron in a metal is one which it is able to traverse only because it is continuously under the action of many molecules—roughly, because the deflection due to the action of one is continually being straightened by the action of the rest. Clearly it would be unwise too implicitly to trust ideas derived from ordinary gases when thinking of electrons in metals.

Magnetic Fields

A magnetic field greatly disturbs the passage of electric currents through gases, especially at low pressures. Anything like a full theory of its action is very complicated, and only a rough outline can be attempted here.

The magnetic field does not affect any motion along the lines of magnetic force. If, however, an ion of mass m and charge e is moving perpendicular to the lines of force, the magnetic field makes it move round a circle. A magnetic force of intensity H produces a force evH on the ion, where v is the ion's speed; this force acts perpendicular to the ion's motion, and so deflects it to follow the circle. If r is the circle's radius, the ion has an acceleration v^2/r towards the circle's centre; thus

$$evH = mv^2/r$$

or

$$r = mv/eH.$$

The time taken by the ion to travel round the circumference $2\pi r$ of the circle is

$$2\pi r/v = 2\pi m/eH,$$

a time independent of the ion's speed. For an electron moving in the earth's magnetic field, this time is rather less than a millionth of a second; for an ordinary ionized atom similarly moving, it is one or two hundredths of a second; in magnetic fields of the size met in laboratories, these times may be cut in the ratio 1:1000, or even less. When an ion moves neither along nor perpendicular to the magnetic field, its motion is the sum of an invariable motion along the lines of force, and a circular motion perpendicular to them; that is, it is a spiral motion round a line of force as axis.

At very low pressures, when collisions with other molecules are comparatively rare events, an ion may be able to travel round several turns of its spiral between collisions; it is then said to spiral freely. At ordinary pressures, however, collisions are much more frequent, and an ion can usually travel along only a tiny arc of its spiral. An electron travels round a turn of a spiral much more rapidly than does an ionized atom, and so is able to spiral freely at higher pressures than the latter.

The magnetic field affects electric currents altogether differently at ordinary pressures and at low. At ordinary pressures an ion travels nearly straight during a free path; the only effect of the magnetic field is slightly to deflect the electric charges which are carrying the electric current, so that the current is not exactly in the direction of the electric field which causes it to flow. At low pressures the magnetic field prevents the ions from being able to travel perpendicular to the lines of force in the direction of an applied electric field, and so chokes currents across the lines of force. Currents do arise which are across the lines of force, but they are not in the direction of the electric field X causing them. The ions move with a spiral motion which slowly drifts across the magnetic field perpendicular to X, with a speed of drift v such that the force evH due to the drift just balances the force eX due to the electric field.

The equations governing the flow of the currents are found as follows. Suppose that most of the molecules are not ionized,

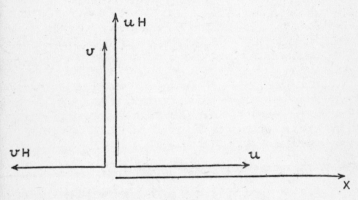

Fig. 27

Electric forces and motions in a transverse magnetic field.

and consider the motion of one sort of ion (an electron, or an ionized molecule) through the rest of the gas. When ions move with speed u across the lines of force, the force euH on them is the same as if an electric field uH acted perpendicular to both u and H. Thus an electric field X perpendicular to H does not simply produce a drift u of the ions in its own direction; the drift u produces an electric field uH perpendicular to X, which leads to a further drift v perpendicular to X; and this drift produces a further electric field vH, acting in a sense to oppose the original field X (see Fig. 27).

Any electric field X produces a drift KX of the ions, where

K is their mobility. The drifts u, v are due to the electric forces $X - vH$, uH respectively; thus

$$u = K(X - vH), v = KuH.$$

Solving these equations for u and v gives

$$u = \frac{KX}{1 + K^2H^2}, v = \frac{K^2HX}{1 + K^2H^2}.$$

Thus when KH is small—which is so at normal pressures—u is nearly KX, as when a magnetic field is absent; v is KH times as big. A current tends to flow in the direction of v, i.e. perpendicular to both X and H, as well as the current in the direction of X; this second current is called the Hall current. It is most easily observed when a current flows in a metal, but it can also be detected when a current flows in a flame.

When KH is large—the case of free spiralling—v becomes large compared with u, and so the chief effect of the electric field (perpendicular to the magnetic lines of force) is to produce diffusion perpendicular to the electric field. The values of u and v are now nearly

$$u = X/KH^2, \quad v = X/H.$$

The electric current due to v is not necessarily large compared with that due to u, even when KH is large. If both electrons and positive ions are free to spiral, they both travel with the same speed v, and since the numbers of the two are usually about equal, the current carried by the one is just cancelled by that due to the other. It is, however, possible for electrons to be free to spiral, but not ions, and in this case the current due to v may be large.

One of the chief applications of this theory is to the E and F layers, high up in the Earth's atmosphere. In the E-layer, electrons are free to spiral in the Earth's magnetic field, but not charged molecules; in the F-layer, both electrons and ionized molecules are free to spiral. Electric currents often flow in these layers; one set of currents flows daily, producing slight daily changes in the Earth's magnetic field, and other currents flow whenever the Aurora Borealis is seen. Such currents need a much bigger electric force to produce them than they would if the magnetic field did not check their flow. The currents are mainly horizontal—they have to flow in relatively thin horizontal layers; but the v-motions which accompany them may lift the F-layer many kilometres during the day.

THE END

SUGGESTIONS FOR FURTHER READING

The reader desiring to learn more about the mathematical side of gas-theory cannot do better than read Jeans' book, *The Kinetic Theory of Gases* (Cambridge University Press, 1940). He must be warned, however, that this book makes considerably greater demands on his mathematical skill than the one which he has been reading. He may also be interested in two books in the Methuen series of Monographs in Physics, Knudsen's *Kinetic Theory of Gases*, and Emeleus's *Conduction of Electricity Through Gases*, which are, however, mainly concerned with the experimental side of the subject.

INDEX